SPECTRUM MATHEMATICS

Third Edition

Brown Book

Thomas J. Richards
Mathematics Teacher
Lamar Junior-Senior High School
Lamar, Missouri

Marjorie Diggs Freeman
Basic Skills Enrichment Program
Shark River Hills School
Neptune, New Jersey

Glencoe
a division of Macmillan Publishing Company
Mission Hills, California

Send all inquiries to:
Glencoe Publishing Company
15319 Chatsworth Street, P.O. Box 9509
Mission Hills, California 91345-9509

Printed in the United States of America

ISBN 0-8445-1422-5

2 3 4 5 6 7 8 9   93 92 91

Table of Contents

NAME ______________________________

SPECTRUM MATHEMATICS, Brown Book

For each chapter there is a PRE-TEST, instructional material, written exercises, verbal problems, and a CHECKUP. There is also a 2-page CHECKUP covering the first half of the book, and a 4-page FINAL CHECKUP covering the entire book.

Record of Checkup Scores

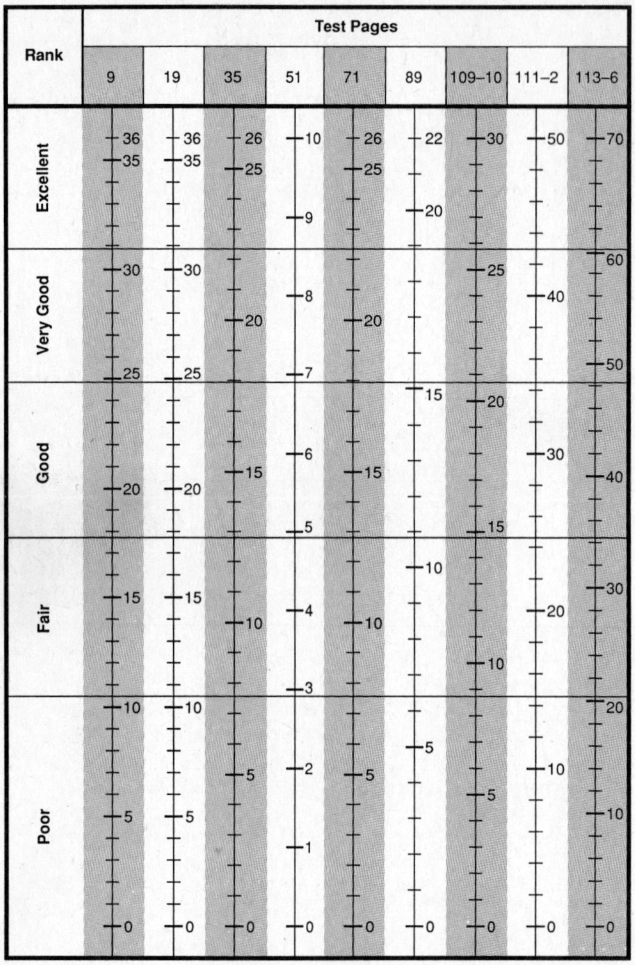

To record the score you receive on each CHECKUP:

(1) Find the vertical scale below the page number of that CHECKUP,

(2) on that vertical scale, draw a ● at the mark which represents your score.

For example, if you score the CHECKUP on page 9 as "My score: 25," draw a ● at the 25-mark on the first vertical scale. A score of 25 would show that your rank is "Good." You can check your progress from one checkup to the next by connecting the dots with a line segment.

Write the numeral for each number.

three  3

one  ____

five  ____

zero ____

two  ____

six  ____

eight  ____

ten  ____

nine 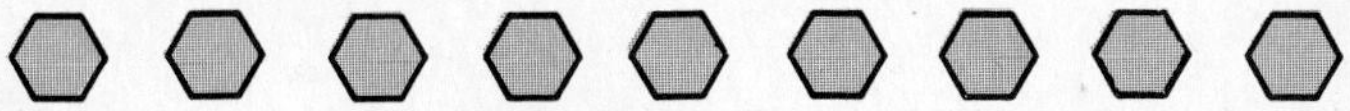 ____

seven  ____

four  ____

Tell how many dots.

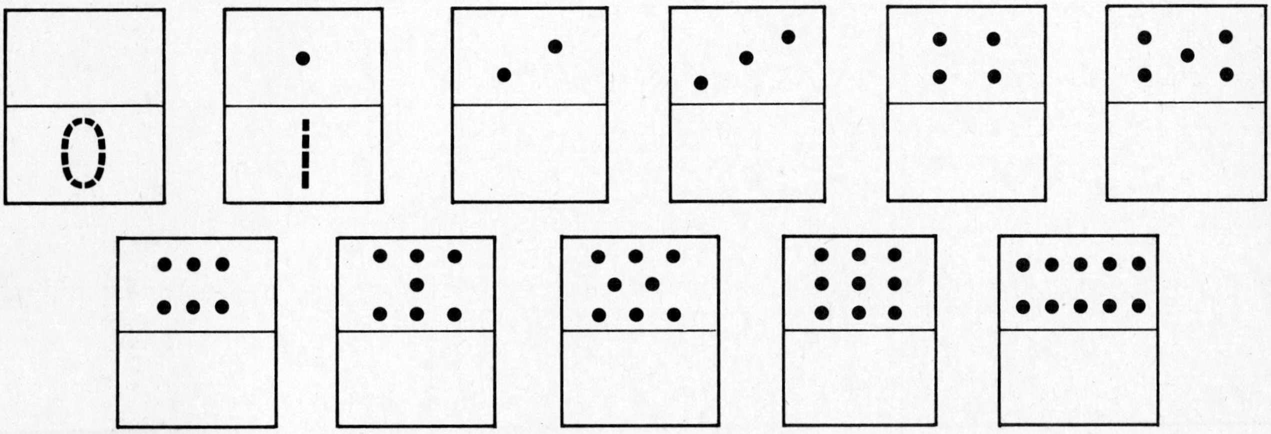

Perfect score: 22 My score: ______

NAME ______________________________

Lesson 2 Facts Through 5

Add or subtract.

$\begin{array}{r} 1 \\ +1 \\ \hline 2 \end{array}$ $\begin{array}{r} 2 \\ -1 \\ \hline 1 \end{array}$ $\begin{array}{r} 2 \\ +1 \\ \hline \end{array}$ $\begin{array}{r} 1 \\ +2 \\ \hline \end{array}$ $\begin{array}{r} 3 \\ -1 \\ \hline \end{array}$ $\begin{array}{r} 3 \\ -2 \\ \hline \end{array}$

$\begin{array}{r} 3 \\ +1 \\ \hline \end{array}$ $\begin{array}{r} 1 \\ +3 \\ \hline \end{array}$

$\begin{array}{r} 4 \\ -1 \\ \hline \end{array}$ $\begin{array}{r} 4 \\ -3 \\ \hline \end{array}$

$\begin{array}{r} 2 \\ +2 \\ \hline \end{array}$

$\begin{array}{r} 4 \\ -2 \\ \hline \end{array}$

$\begin{array}{r} 4 \\ +0 \\ \hline \end{array}$ $\begin{array}{r} 0 \\ +4 \\ \hline \end{array}$

$\begin{array}{r} 4 \\ -0 \\ \hline \end{array}$ $\begin{array}{r} 4 \\ -4 \\ \hline \end{array}$

$\begin{array}{r} 3 \\ +2 \\ \hline \end{array}$ $\begin{array}{r} 2 \\ +3 \\ \hline \end{array}$

$\begin{array}{r} 5 \\ -2 \\ \hline \end{array}$ $\begin{array}{r} 5 \\ -3 \\ \hline \end{array}$

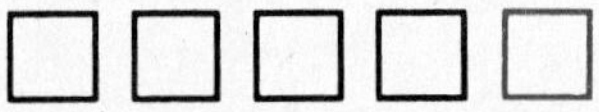

$\begin{array}{r} 4 \\ +1 \\ \hline \end{array}$ $\begin{array}{r} 1 \\ +4 \\ \hline \end{array}$

$\begin{array}{r} 5 \\ -1 \\ \hline \end{array}$ $\begin{array}{r} 5 \\ -4 \\ \hline \end{array}$

$\begin{array}{r} 5 \\ +0 \\ \hline \end{array}$ $\begin{array}{r} 0 \\ +5 \\ \hline \end{array}$

$\begin{array}{r} 5 \\ -0 \\ \hline \end{array}$ $\begin{array}{r} 5 \\ -5 \\ \hline \end{array}$

Perfect score: 28 My score: ________

NAME ______________________

Lesson 3 Facts for 6 and 7

Add or subtract.

$5 + 1 = 6$ $1 + 5$

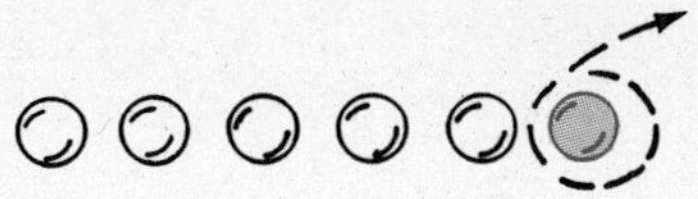

$6 - 1 = 5$

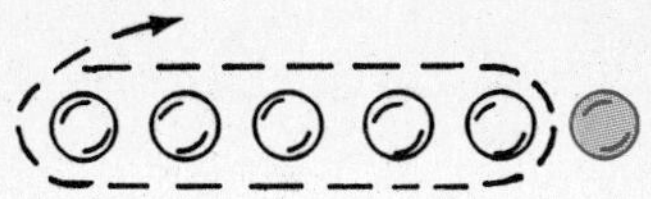

$6 - 5$

$3 + 3$ $6 - 3$

$4 + 2$ $2 + 4$ $6 - 2$ $6 - 4$

$4 + 3$ $3 + 4$

$7 - 3$ $7 - 4$

$5 + 2$ $2 + 5$

$7 - 2$ $7 - 5$

$6 + 1$ $1 + 6$

$7 - 1$ $7 - 6$

$3 + 3$ $5 + 2$ $6 + 0$

$7 - 7$ $7 - 4$ $6 - 2$

Perfect score: 28   My score: ________

NAME ______________________

Lesson 4 Facts for 8

Add or subtract.

$\begin{array}{r} 5 \\ +3 \\ \hline 8 \end{array}$ $\begin{array}{r} 3 \\ +5 \\ \hline \end{array}$

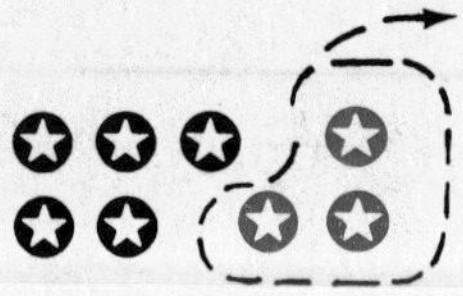

$\begin{array}{r} 8 \\ -3 \\ \hline 5 \end{array}$

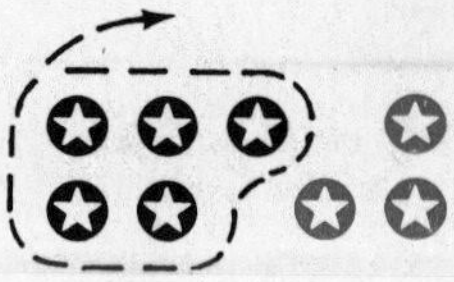

$\begin{array}{r} 8 \\ -5 \\ \hline \end{array}$

$\begin{array}{r} 4 \\ +4 \\ \hline \end{array}$

$\begin{array}{r} 8 \\ -4 \\ \hline \end{array}$

$\begin{array}{r} 6 \\ +2 \\ \hline \end{array}$ $\begin{array}{r} 2 \\ +6 \\ \hline \end{array}$

$\begin{array}{r} 8 \\ -2 \\ \hline \end{array}$ $\begin{array}{r} 8 \\ -6 \\ \hline \end{array}$

$\begin{array}{r} 7 \\ +1 \\ \hline \end{array}$ $\begin{array}{r} 1 \\ +7 \\ \hline \end{array}$

$\begin{array}{r} 8 \\ -1 \\ \hline \end{array}$ $\begin{array}{r} 8 \\ -7 \\ \hline \end{array}$

$\begin{array}{r} 2 \\ +6 \\ \hline \end{array}$ $\begin{array}{r} 4 \\ +3 \\ \hline \end{array}$ $\begin{array}{r} 5 \\ +1 \\ \hline \end{array}$ $\begin{array}{r} 3 \\ +5 \\ \hline \end{array}$ $\begin{array}{r} 7 \\ +1 \\ \hline \end{array}$ $\begin{array}{r} 0 \\ +8 \\ \hline \end{array}$

$\begin{array}{r} 8 \\ -1 \\ \hline \end{array}$ $\begin{array}{r} 7 \\ -6 \\ \hline \end{array}$ $\begin{array}{r} 8 \\ -5 \\ \hline \end{array}$ $\begin{array}{r} 6 \\ -3 \\ \hline \end{array}$ $\begin{array}{r} 8 \\ -0 \\ \hline \end{array}$ $\begin{array}{r} 8 \\ -2 \\ \hline \end{array}$

Perfect score: 26 My score: ________

NAME ______________________

Lesson 5 Facts for 9

Add or subtract.

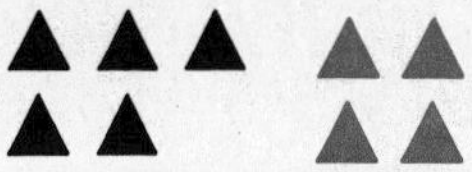

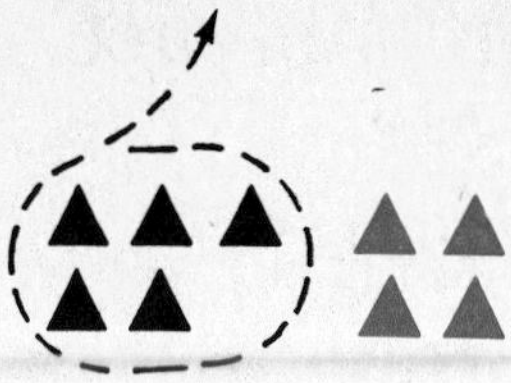

5 + 4 = 9	4 + 5 =	9 − 4 = 5	9 − 5 =

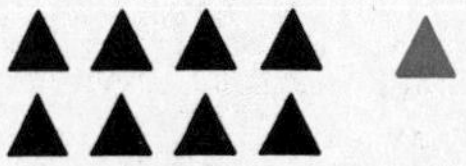

6 + 3 =	3 + 6 =	7 + 2 =	2 + 7 =	8 + 1 =	1 + 8 =
9 − 3 =	9 − 6 =	9 − 2 =	9 − 7 =	9 − 1 =	9 − 8 =

5 + 4 =	2 + 7 =	6 + 1 =	9 + 0 =	1 + 8 =	4 + 4 =
9 − 5 =	7 − 3 =	9 − 8 =	9 − 3 =	9 − 9 =	9 − 0 =

Perfect score: 28 My score: ________

Lesson 6 Facts for 10

NAME ______________________

Add or subtract.

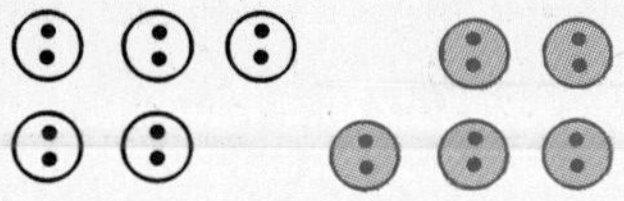

$\begin{array}{r} 5 \\ +5 \\ \hline 10 \end{array}$

$\begin{array}{r} 10 \\ -5 \\ \hline 5 \end{array}$

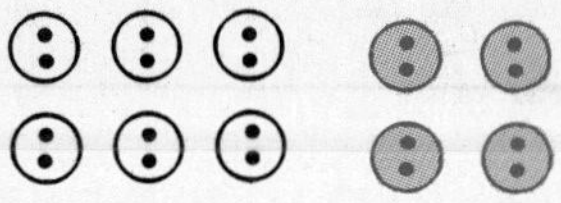

$\begin{array}{r} 6 \\ +4 \\ \hline \end{array}$ $\quad$ $\begin{array}{r} 4 \\ +6 \\ \hline \end{array}$

$\begin{array}{r} 10 \\ -4 \\ \hline \end{array}$ $\quad$ $\begin{array}{r} 10 \\ -6 \\ \hline \end{array}$

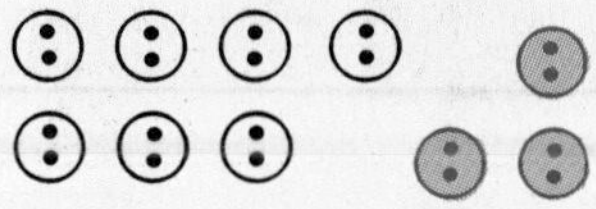

$\begin{array}{r} 7 \\ +3 \\ \hline \end{array}$ $\quad$ $\begin{array}{r} 3 \\ +7 \\ \hline \end{array}$

$\begin{array}{r} 10 \\ -3 \\ \hline \end{array}$ $\quad$ $\begin{array}{r} 10 \\ -7 \\ \hline \end{array}$

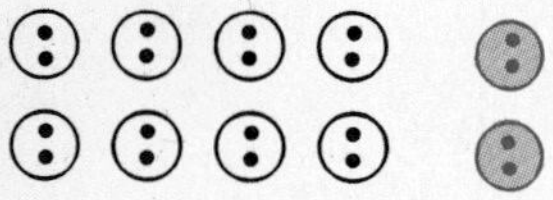

$\begin{array}{r} 8 \\ +2 \\ \hline \end{array}$ $\quad$ $\begin{array}{r} 2 \\ +8 \\ \hline \end{array}$

$\begin{array}{r} 10 \\ -2 \\ \hline \end{array}$ $\quad$ $\begin{array}{r} 10 \\ -8 \\ \hline \end{array}$

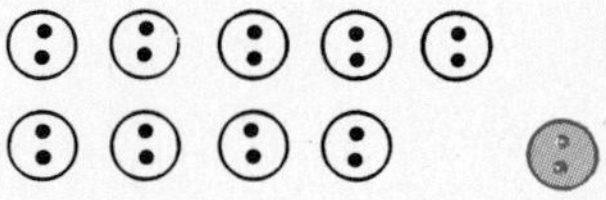

$\begin{array}{r} 9 \\ +1 \\ \hline \end{array}$ $\quad$ $\begin{array}{r} 1 \\ +9 \\ \hline \end{array}$

$\begin{array}{r} 10 \\ -1 \\ \hline \end{array}$ $\quad$ $\begin{array}{r} 10 \\ -9 \\ \hline \end{array}$

$\begin{array}{r} 4 \\ +6 \\ \hline \end{array}$ $\quad$ $\begin{array}{r} 5 \\ +5 \\ \hline \end{array}$ $\quad$ $\begin{array}{r} 9 \\ +1 \\ \hline \end{array}$ $\quad$ $\begin{array}{r} 10 \\ -8 \\ \hline \end{array}$ $\quad$ $\begin{array}{r} 10 \\ -3 \\ \hline \end{array}$ $\quad$ $\begin{array}{r} 10 \\ -0 \\ \hline \end{array}$

Perfect score: 24 My score: ________

NAME ____________________

Lesson 7 Facts Through 10

Add.

5	4	1	5	4	4
+4	+3	+2	+3	+6	+4
9					

0	4	8	9	8	2
+6	+1	+1	+1	+2	+2

2	5	1	5	4	6
+7	+2	+6	+5	+5	+2

Subtract.

10	8	5	7	4	10
−6	−2	−3	−6	−3	−5
4					

9	10	7	8	10	8
−3	−2	−2	−6	−9	−8

10	9	9	8	10	7
−4	−6	−8	−1	−7	−4

Perfect score: 36 My score: ________

Problem Solving

Solve each problem.

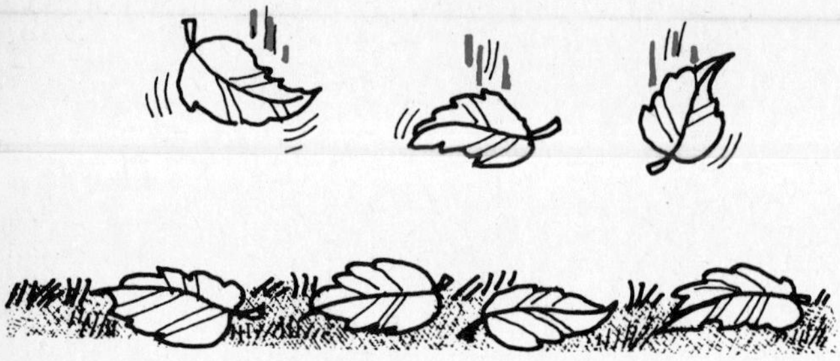

	4	leaves on the ground
+	3	leaves falling
	7	leaves in all

		balls in all
−		balls falling
		balls not falling

		fish by a rock
+		more fish coming
		fish in all

		pencils in all
−		pencils taken
		pencils not taken

		puppies on a rug
+		more puppies coming
		puppies in all

Perfect score: 5 My score: ______

NAME ____________________

Chapter 1 Checkup

Add.

2	7	4	6	2	0
+4	+3	+5	+2	+3	+4

4	1	2	3	6	2
+3	+5	+8	+3	+4	+1

3	7	8	5	3	5
+1	+0	+1	+2	+6	+5

Subtract.

3	5	10	9	7	10
−3	−2	− 6	−2	−3	− 5

9	8	1	6	8	10
−1	−7	−0	−4	−5	− 8

9	4	6	7	10	8
−6	−3	−3	−5	− 9	−4

Perfect score: 36 My score: __________

PRE-TEST

Tell how many.

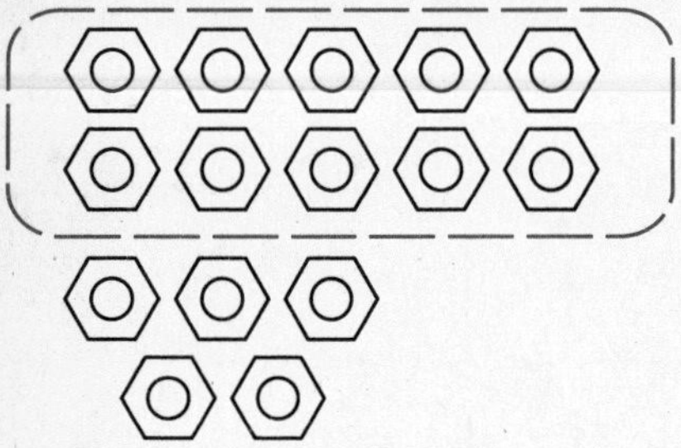

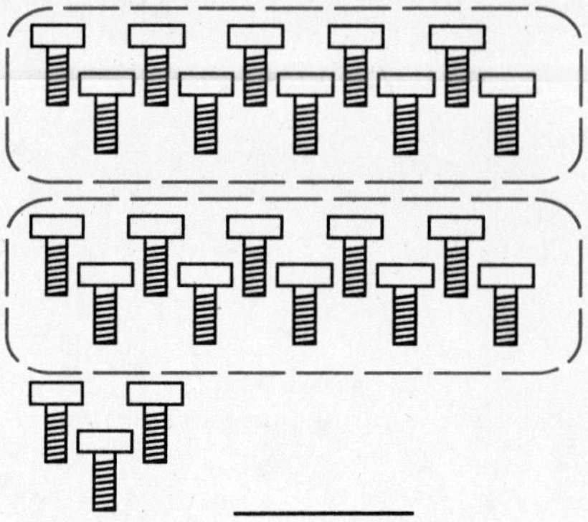

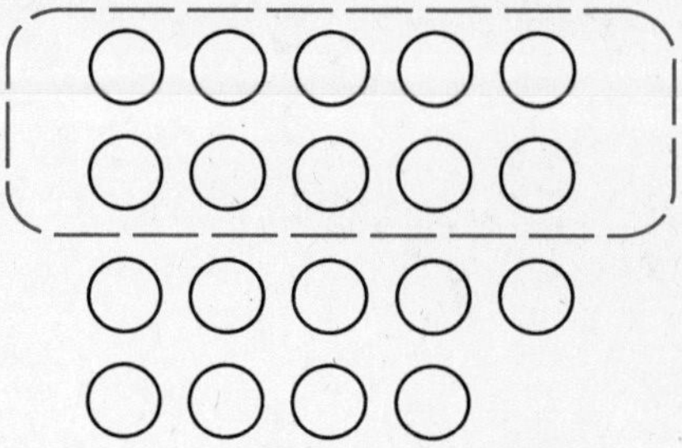

_____   _____   _____

Complete.

1 ten 3 ones = _____   2 tens = _____

3 tens 4 ones = _____   4 tens 6 ones = _____

8 tens = _____   7 tens 9 ones = _____

Name the next four numbers.

6, 7, 8, _____, _____, _____, _____

24, 25, 26, _____, _____, _____, _____

50, 51, 52, _____, _____, _____, _____

67, 68, 69, _____, _____, _____, _____

Perfect score: 25   My score: _____

NAME ______________________

Lesson 1 Numbers 11 Through 18

1¢

10¢

10¢

Complete.

1 ten 1 one = 11

____ ten ____ ones = _____

____ ten ____ ones = _____

____ ten ____ ones = _____

____ ten ____ ones = _____

____ ten ____ ones = _____

____ ten ____ ones = _____

____ ten ____ ones = _____

Perfect score: 8 My score: ______

NAME ______________________

Lesson 2 Numbers 19 Through 39

Complete.

2 tens = 20

____ tens ____ ones = ______

____ tens ____ ones = ______

____ tens ____ ones = ______

____ tens = ______

____ tens ____ ones = ______

____ tens ____ ones = ______

____ tens ____ ones = ______

Perfect score: 8 My score: ______

NAME ____________________

Lesson 3 Numbers 40 Through 99

Complete.

4 tens = 40

____ tens ____ ones = ______

____ tens ____ ones = ______

____ tens ____ ones = ______

____ tens = ______

____ tens ____ ones = ______

____ tens ____ ones = ______

____ tens ____ ones = ______

Perfect score: 8 My score: ______

Numbers 40 Through 99

Complete.

4 tens 5 ones = 45

____ tens ____ ones = ____

____ tens = ____

____ tens ____ ones = ____

____ tens ____ ones = ____

____ tens ____ ones = ____

____ tens = ____

____ tens ____ ones = ____

Perfect score: 8 My score: ____

NAME ______________________

Lesson 4 Numbers Through 99

Complete.

4 tens 6 ones = 46

2 tens 1 one = ____

1 ten 2 ones = ____

5 tens 7 ones = ____

3 tens 7 ones = ____

1 ten 9 ones = ____

2 tens 4 ones = ____

8 tens 8 ones = ____

9 tens = ____

6 tens 7 ones = ____

6 tens = ____

7 tens 2 ones = ____

5 tens 3 ones = ____

9 tens 5 ones = ____

7 tens 8 ones = ____

4 tens 1 one = ____

1 ten 1 one = ____

3 tens 4 ones = ____

8 tens 4 ones = ____

6 tens 6 ones = ____

3 tens 5 ones = ____

8 tens 9 ones = ____

4 tens 9 ones = ____

2 tens = ____

9 tens 6 ones = ____

5 tens = ____

Perfect score: 26 My score: ________

Numbers Through 99

Name numbers in order.

0	1								
10					15				
									29
			33						
40							47		
				54					

Connect the dots in order.

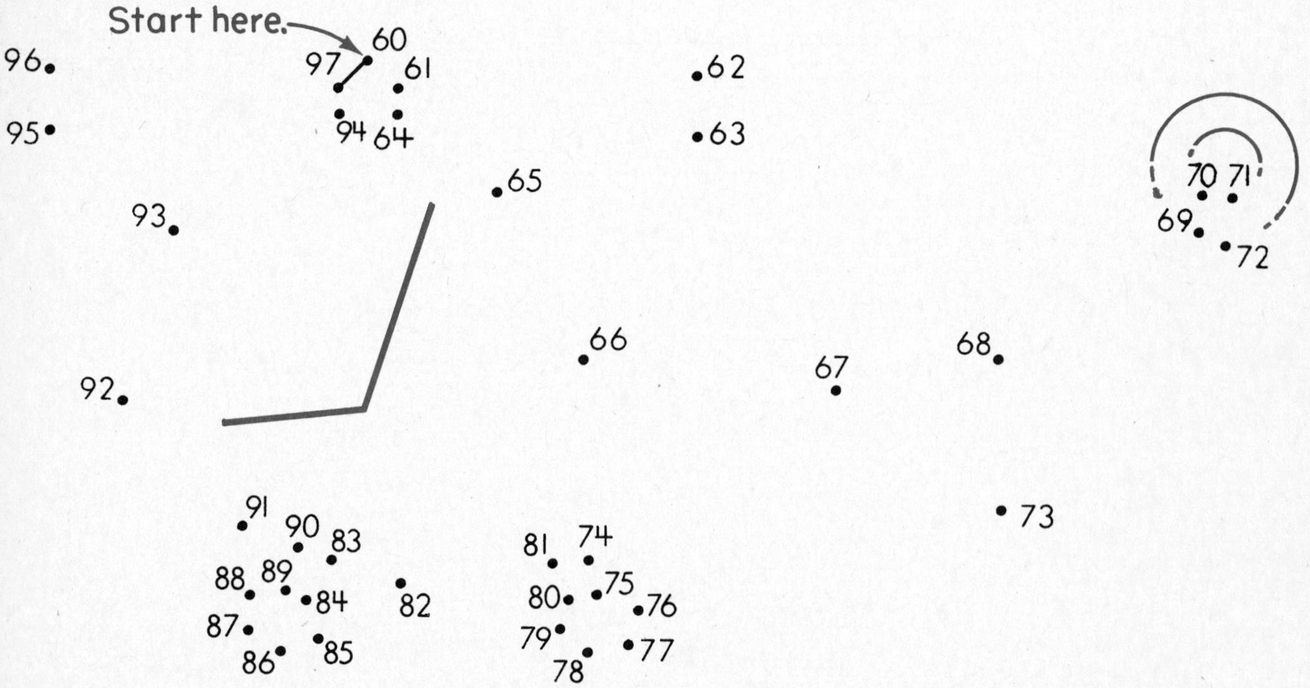

Perfect score: 61 My score: ______

Lesson 5 Numbers Through 99

NAME ____________________

Name the next four numbers.

6, 7, 8, 9, 10, 11, 12

22, 23, 24, ____, ____, ____, ____

37, 38, 39, ____, ____, ____, ____

15, 16, 17, ____, ____, ____, ____

51, 52, 53, ____, ____, ____, ____

44, 45, 46, ____, ____, ____, ____

76, 77, 78, ____, ____, ____, ____

82, 83, 84, ____, ____, ____, ____

68, 69, 70, ____, ____, ____, ____

86, 87, 88, ____, ____, ____, ____

55, 56, 57, ____, ____, ____, ____

93, 94, 95, ____, ____, ____, ____

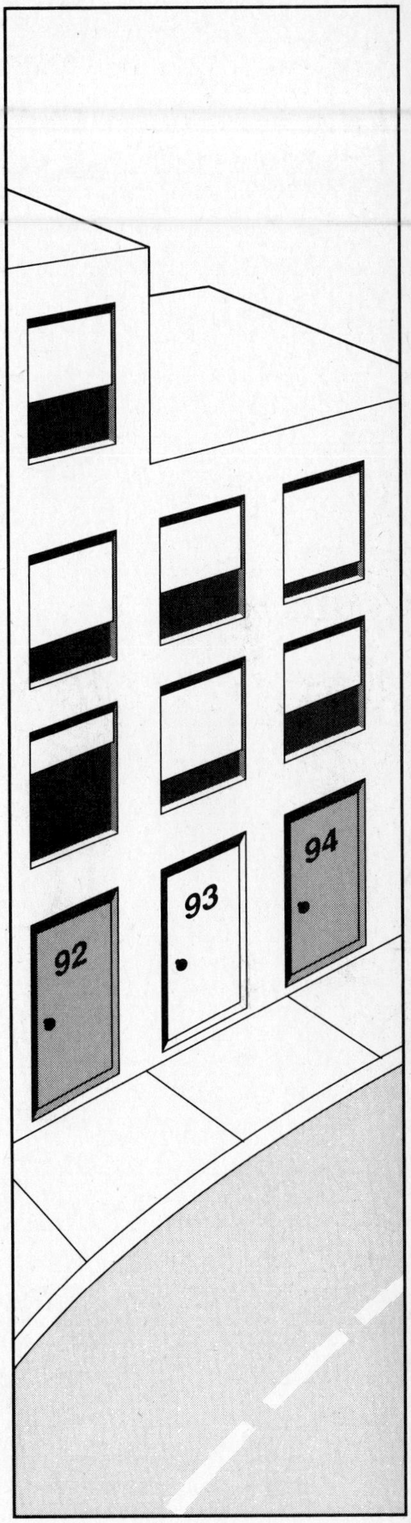

Perfect score: 48 My score: ____

Lesson 6 Skip Counting

NAME ____________________

Count by 10.

10, 20, 30, ____, ____,

____, ____, ____, ____

Count by 5.

5, 10, 15, ____, ____,

____, ____, ____, ____, ____,

____, ____, ____, ____, ____

Perfect score: 24 My score: ________

NAME ______________________

Chapter 2 Checkup

Complete.

2 tens 8 ones = _____

3 tens 1 one = _____

7 tens = _____

6 tens 6 ones = _____

9 tens = _____

5 tens = _____

4 tens 5 ones = _____

8 tens 2 ones = _____

9 tens 8 ones = _____

7 tens 9 ones = _____

Name the next four numbers.

4, 5, 6, _____, _____, _____, _____

37, 38, 39, _____, _____, _____, _____

53, 54, 55, _____, _____, _____, _____

61, 62, 63, _____, _____, _____, _____

78, 79, 80, _____, _____, _____, _____

86, 87, 88, _____, _____, _____, _____

Perfect score: 34 My score: _______

NAME ______________________

Add.

3	5	2	7	4	6
+4	+4	+8	+2	+6	+2
5	3	9	6	8	2
+7	+8	+4	+6	+5	+9
7	9	8	4	8	6
+7	+6	+7	+9	+8	+8

Subtract.

6	5	9	8	10	7
−3	−4	−7	−2	− 7	−0
11	13	11	12	13	12
− 7	− 6	− 5	− 4	− 4	− 9
14	17	16	14	15	18
− 5	− 9	− 7	− 7	− 6	− 9

Perfect score: 36 My score: __________

NAME ____________________

Add.

2 +9 11	* * * * * * * * * * *	9 +2	
3 +8	* * * * * * * * * * *	8 +3	
6 +5	* * * * * * * * * * *	5 +6	
4 +7	* * * * * * * * * * *	7 +4	
8 +4	* * * * * * * * * * * *	4 +8	
7 +5	* * * * * * * * * * * *	5 +7	
9 +3	* * * * * * * * * * * *	3 +9	
6 +6	* * * * * * * * * * * *		

Add.

8 +3	6 +6	9 +3	3 +8	4 +7	2 +9
5 +7	8 +4	7 +5	5 +6	9 +2	4 +8

Perfect score: 27   My score: ________

Problem Solving

Solve each problem.

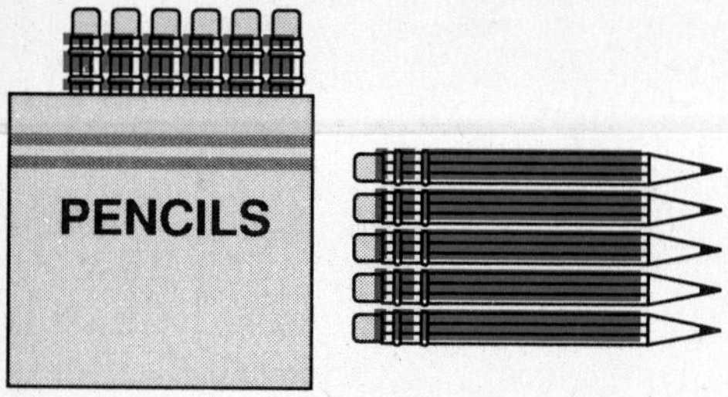

$$\begin{array}{r} 6 \\ +5 \\ \hline \end{array}$$

pencils in a box

more pencils

pencils in all

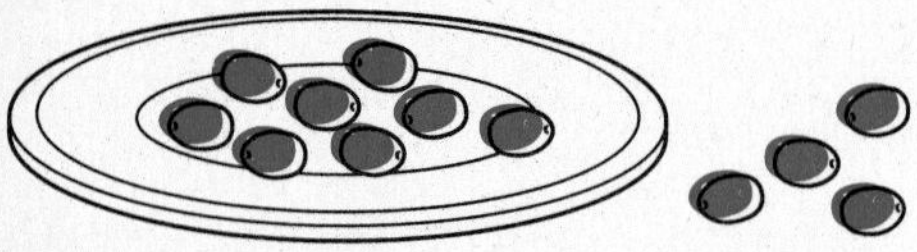

grapes on a plate

more grapes

grapes in all

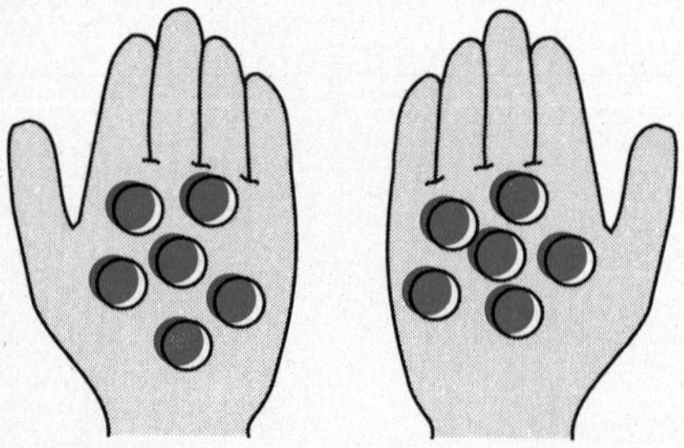

marbles in one hand

marbles in the other hand

marbles in all

people at the table

more people coming in

people in all

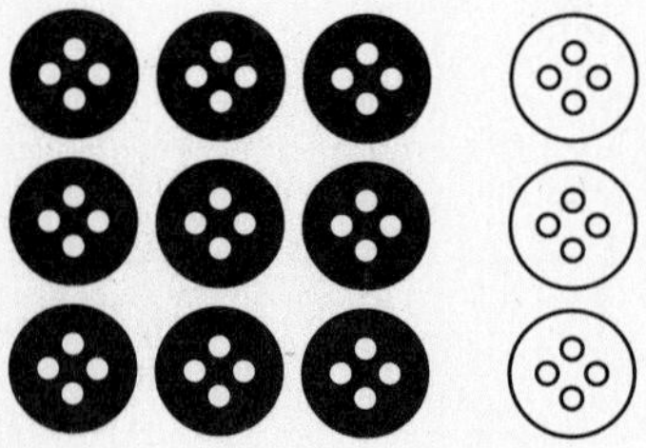

black buttons

white buttons

buttons in all

Perfect score: 5 My score: ______

NAME ____________________

Lesson 2 Subtraction Facts Through 12

Subtract.

11 − 9	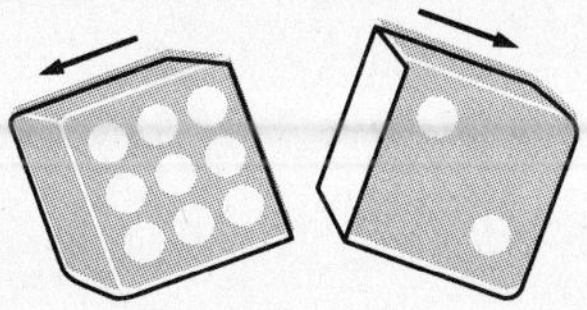	11 − 2	11 − 8	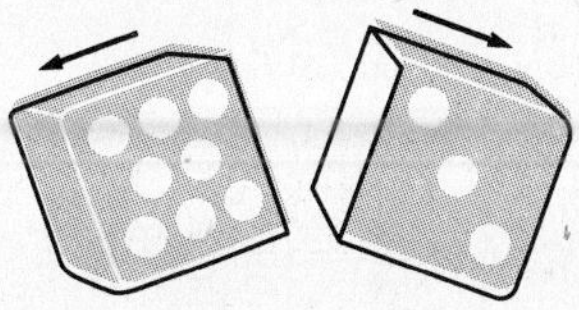	11 − 3
11 − 6	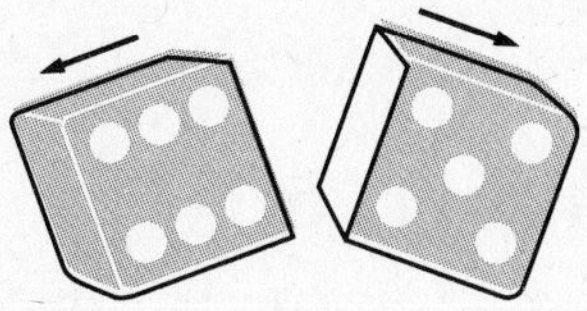	11 − 5	11 − 7	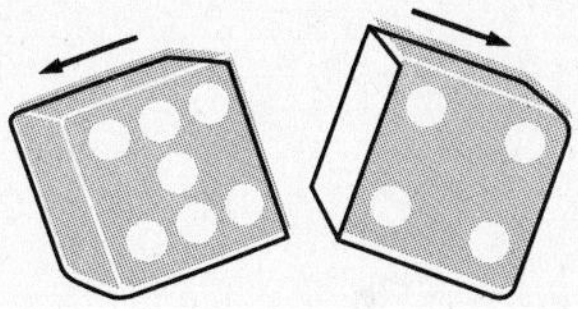	11 − 4
12 − 8	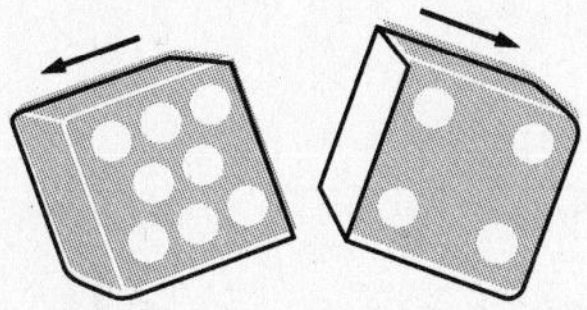	12 − 4	12 − 7		12 − 5
12 − 9	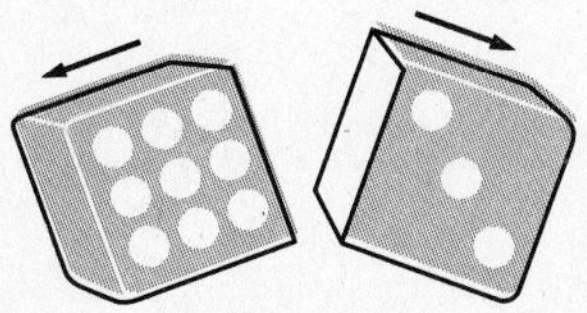	12 − 3	12 − 6	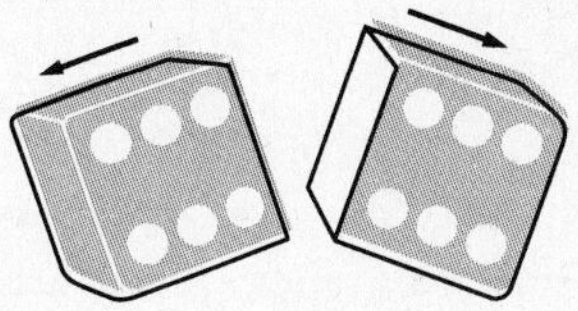	

Subtract.

11 − 3	11 − 6	12 − 3	11 − 8	12 − 7	12 − 9
11 − 7	12 − 4	12 − 5	12 − 6	11 − 2	12 − 8

Perfect score: 27 My score: __________

Problem Solving

Solve each problem.

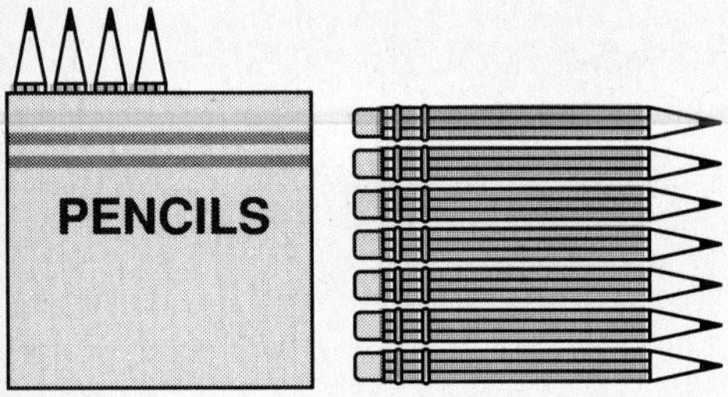

$$\begin{array}{r} 11 \\ -\ 4 \\ \hline \end{array}$$

pencils in all

pencils in the box

pencils not in the box

people in all

people are leaving

people are staying

oranges in all

oranges in the bowl

oranges not in the bowl

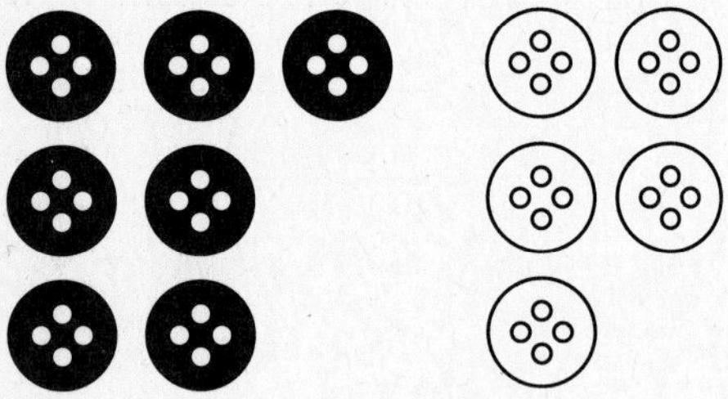

buttons in all

black buttons

white buttons

candles in all

candles lit

candles not lit

Perfect score: 5 My score: ________

NAME ____________________

Lesson 3 Addition Through 14

Add.

6
+7
13

7
+6

5
+8

8
+5

9
+4

4
+9

9
+5

5
+9

8
+6

6
+8

7
+7

Add.

7	5	9	8	4	5
+7	+8	+4	+6	+9	+9
8	6	9	6	7	6
+5	+8	+5	+6	+6	+7

Perfect score: 23 My score: ________

NAME ____________________

Lesson 4 Subtraction Facts Through 14

Subtract.

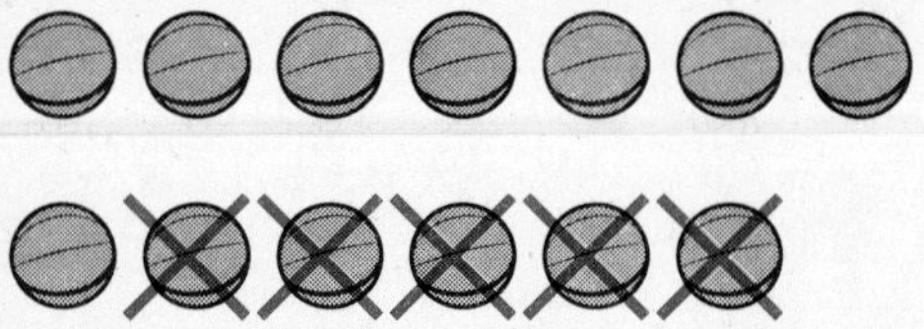

$$\begin{array}{r} 13 \\ -\ 5 \\ \hline 8 \end{array}$$

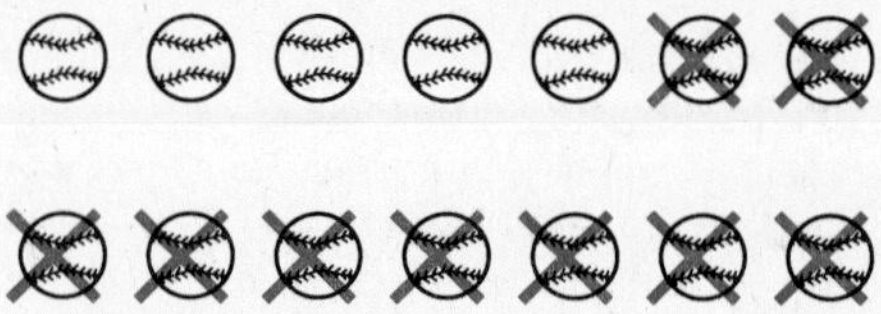

$$\begin{array}{r} 14 \\ -\ 9 \\ \hline 5 \end{array}$$

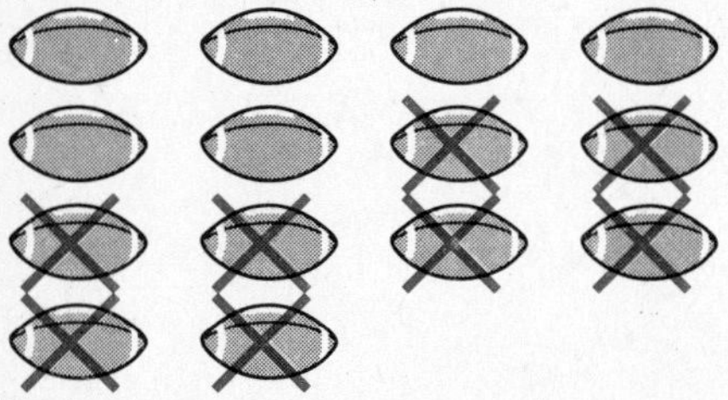

$$\begin{array}{r} 14 \\ -\ 8 \\ \hline \end{array}$$

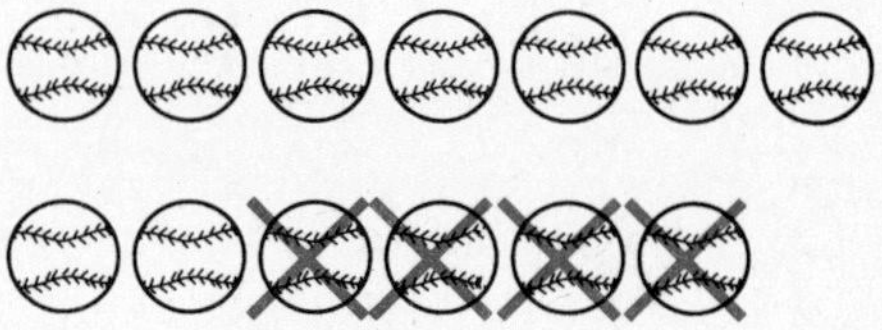

$$\begin{array}{r} 13 \\ -\ 4 \\ \hline \end{array}$$

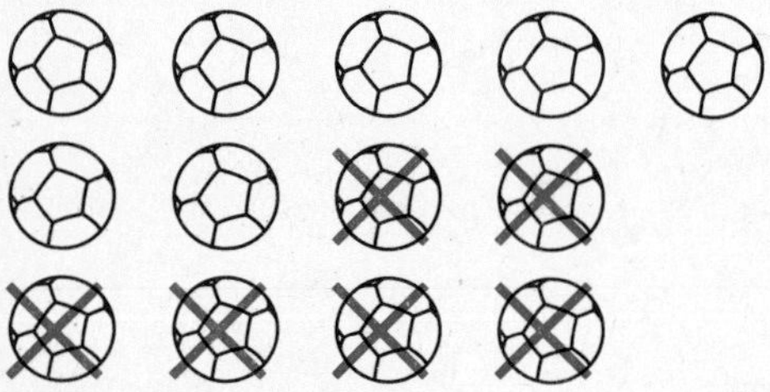

$$\begin{array}{r} 13 \\ -\ 6 \\ \hline \end{array}$$

$$\begin{array}{r} 14 \\ -\ 5 \\ \hline \end{array}$$

Subtract.

$$\begin{array}{r} 12 \\ -\ 7 \\ \hline 5 \end{array} \qquad \begin{array}{r} 10 \\ -\ 2 \\ \hline \end{array} \qquad \begin{array}{r} 13 \\ -\ 4 \\ \hline \end{array} \qquad \begin{array}{r} 14 \\ -\ 9 \\ \hline \end{array} \qquad \begin{array}{r} 11 \\ -\ 8 \\ \hline \end{array} \qquad \begin{array}{r} 14 \\ -\ 5 \\ \hline \end{array}$$

$$\begin{array}{r} 14 \\ -\ 6 \\ \hline \end{array} \qquad \begin{array}{r} 12 \\ -\ 8 \\ \hline \end{array} \qquad \begin{array}{r} 13 \\ -\ 5 \\ \hline \end{array} \qquad \begin{array}{r} 10 \\ -\ 6 \\ \hline \end{array} \qquad \begin{array}{r} 13 \\ -\ 6 \\ \hline \end{array} \qquad \begin{array}{r} 13 \\ -\ 7 \\ \hline \end{array}$$

$$\begin{array}{r} 11 \\ -\ 6 \\ \hline \end{array} \qquad \begin{array}{r} 13 \\ -\ 9 \\ \hline \end{array} \qquad \begin{array}{r} 14 \\ -\ 8 \\ \hline \end{array} \qquad \begin{array}{r} 12 \\ -\ 3 \\ \hline \end{array} \qquad \begin{array}{r} 14 \\ -\ 7 \\ \hline \end{array} \qquad \begin{array}{r} 13 \\ -\ 8 \\ \hline \end{array}$$

Perfect score: 24 My score: ________

Lesson 5 Addition Facts Through 18

NAME ______________________

Add.

$\begin{array}{r} 6 \\ +9 \\ \hline 15 \end{array}$

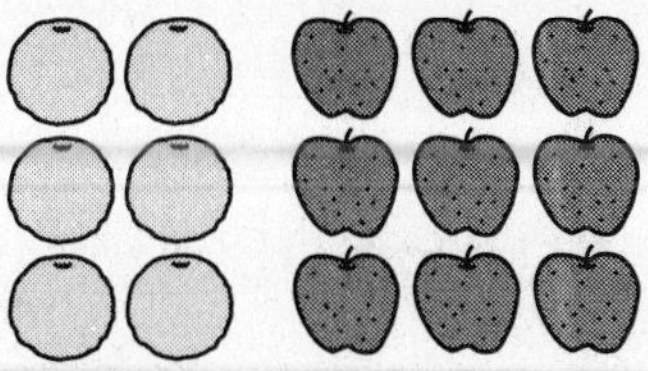

$\begin{array}{r} 9 \\ +6 \\ \hline \end{array}$

$\begin{array}{r} 8 \\ +7 \\ \hline \end{array}$

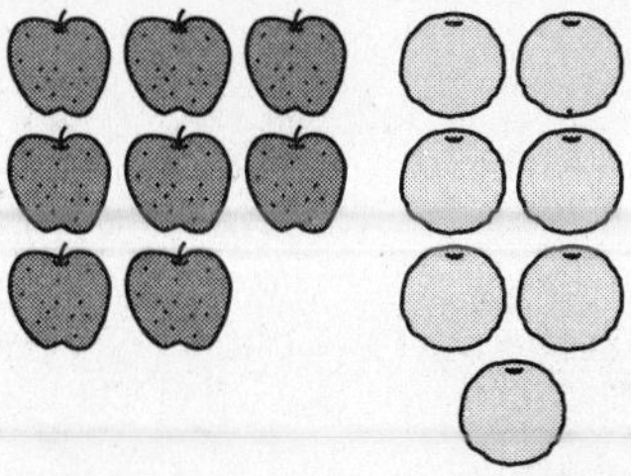

$\begin{array}{r} 7 \\ +8 \\ \hline \end{array}$

$\begin{array}{r} 9 \\ +7 \\ \hline \end{array}$

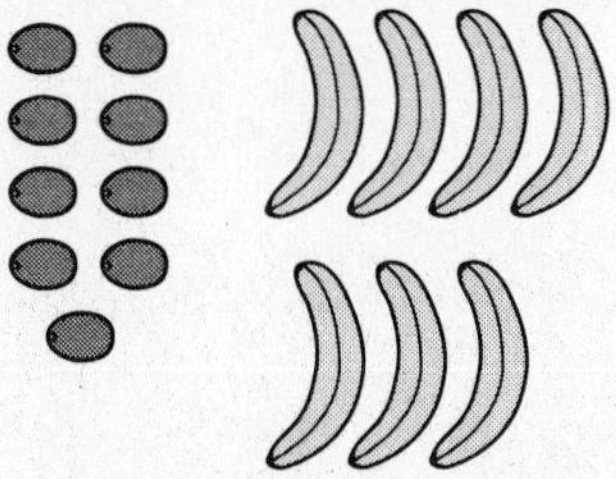

$\begin{array}{r} 7 \\ +9 \\ \hline \end{array}$

$\begin{array}{r} 8 \\ +9 \\ \hline \end{array}$

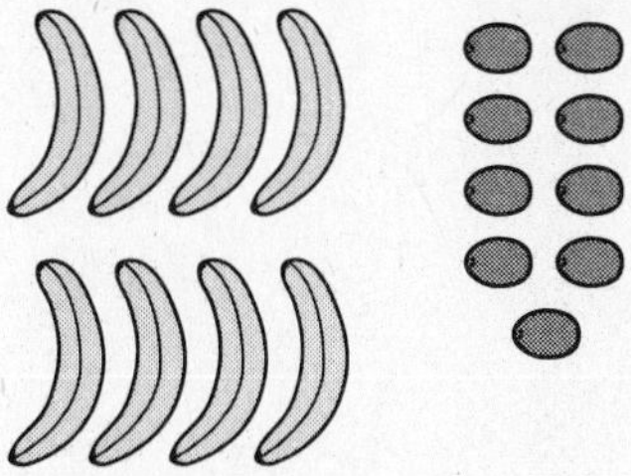

$\begin{array}{r} 9 \\ +8 \\ \hline \end{array}$

$\begin{array}{r} 8 \\ +8 \\ \hline \end{array}$

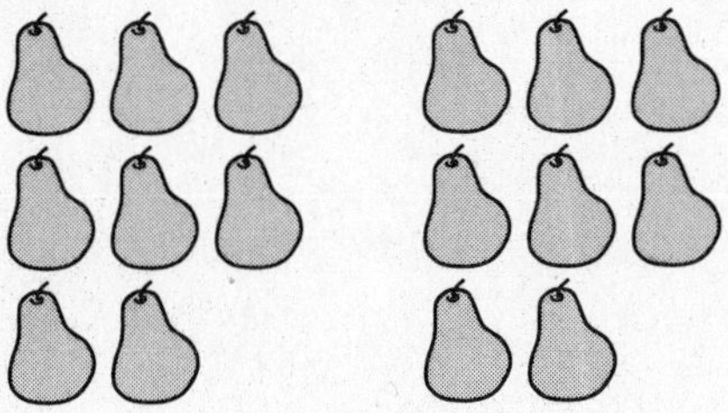

$\begin{array}{r} 9 \\ +9 \\ \hline \end{array}$

Add.

$\begin{array}{r} 9 \\ +6 \\ \hline 15 \end{array}$ $\begin{array}{r} 7 \\ +8 \\ \hline \end{array}$ $\begin{array}{r} 9 \\ +9 \\ \hline \end{array}$ $\begin{array}{r} 7 \\ +9 \\ \hline \end{array}$ $\begin{array}{r} 8 \\ +9 \\ \hline \end{array}$ $\begin{array}{r} 6 \\ +9 \\ \hline \end{array}$

$\begin{array}{r} 9 \\ +8 \\ \hline \end{array}$ $\begin{array}{r} 8 \\ +8 \\ \hline \end{array}$ $\begin{array}{r} 9 \\ +7 \\ \hline \end{array}$ $\begin{array}{r} 8 \\ +7 \\ \hline \end{array}$ $\begin{array}{r} 9 \\ +5 \\ \hline \end{array}$ $\begin{array}{r} 7 \\ +7 \\ \hline \end{array}$

$\begin{array}{r} 9 \\ +3 \\ \hline \end{array}$ $\begin{array}{r} 8 \\ +5 \\ \hline \end{array}$ $\begin{array}{r} 7 \\ +6 \\ \hline \end{array}$ $\begin{array}{r} 8 \\ +6 \\ \hline \end{array}$ $\begin{array}{r} 9 \\ +4 \\ \hline \end{array}$ $\begin{array}{r} 7 \\ +5 \\ \hline \end{array}$

Perfect score: 28 My score: ________

Problem Solving

Solve each problem.

	9	black sheep
+	9	white sheep
		sheep in all

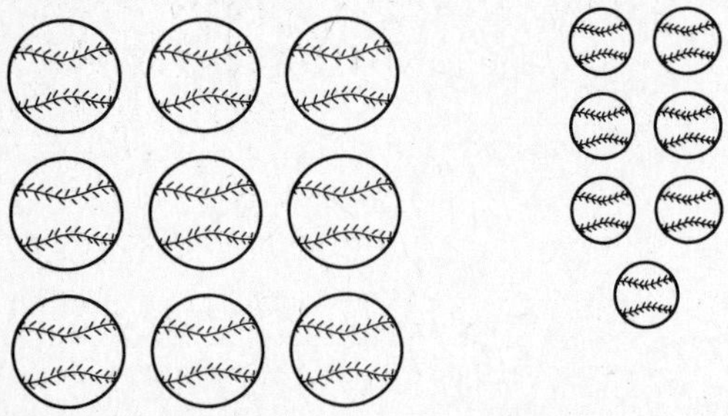

softballs

baseballs

softballs and baseballs

glasses of milk

empty glasses

glasses in all

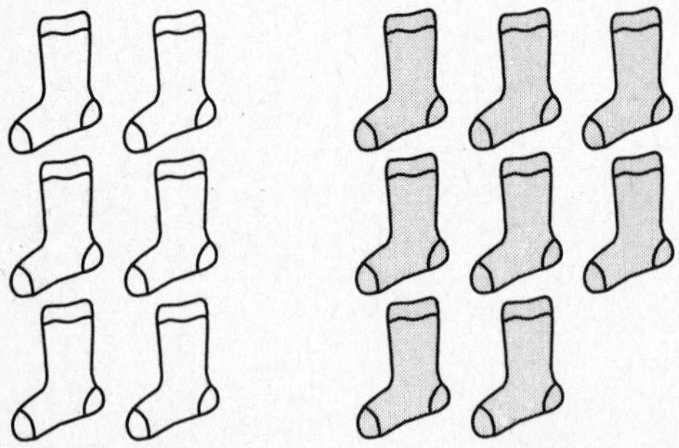

white socks

gray socks

socks in all

bow ties

regular ties

ties in all

Perfect score: 5 My score: ______

Lesson 6 Subtraction Facts Through 18

Subtract.

$$\begin{array}{r} 15 \\ -\ 7 \\ \hline 8 \end{array}$$

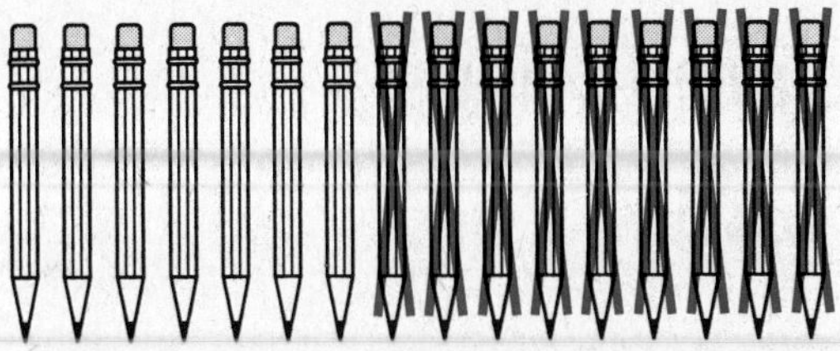

$$\begin{array}{r} 16 \\ -\ 9 \\ \hline \end{array}$$

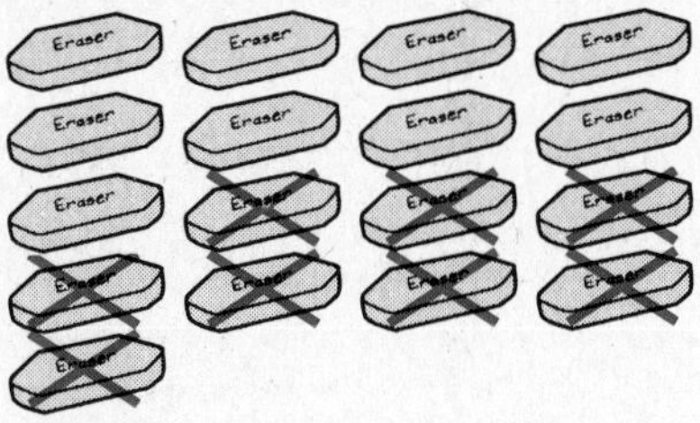

$$\begin{array}{r} 17 \\ -\ 8 \\ \hline \end{array}$$

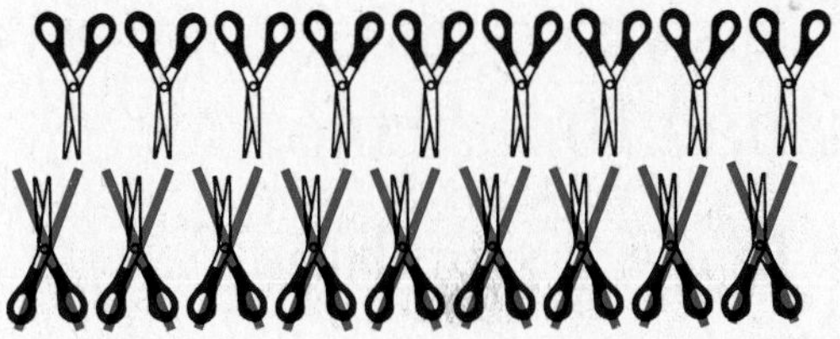

$$\begin{array}{r} 18 \\ -\ 9 \\ \hline \end{array}$$

Subtract.

18 − 9 = 9	13 − 5	16 − 8	17 − 9	14 − 6	13 − 9
17 − 8	15 − 9	14 − 5	13 − 6	16 − 7	12 − 4
14 − 7	15 − 8	16 − 9	12 − 7	15 − 7	13 − 4
15 − 6	14 − 8	12 − 3	13 − 9	14 − 9	11 − 3

Perfect score: 28 My score: ________

Problem Solving

Solve each problem.

There are 12 dogs.

3 run away.

How many dogs are left?

$$\begin{array}{r} 12 \\ -\ 3 \\ \hline 9 \end{array}$$

Roger has 10 marbles.

Roger loses 3 marbles.

How many marbles are left?

Mary has 16 black shoes.

Mike has 8 black shoes.

How many more shoes does Mary have than Mike?

There are 14 cows in the field.

9 cows come to the barn.

How many cows are left in the field?

There are 18 horses running.

There are 9 horses standing.

How many more horses are running than standing?

Perfect score: 5 My score: ______

Lesson 7 Mixed Practice Facts Through 18

Add.

9	5	7	4	9	7
+7	+9	+8	+9	+9	+7
16					

6	8	9	7	8	7
+9	+6	+5	+9	+9	+6

8	6	9	8	9	8
+8	+8	+6	+5	+8	+7

Subtract.

16	10	16	12	14	16
− 9	− 8	− 8	− 6	− 8	− 7
7					

11	14	15	12	17	10
− 7	− 9	− 9	− 8	− 8	− 5

14	17	13	15	18	13
− 7	− 9	− 7	− 8	− 9	− 8

Perfect score: 36 My score: ________

Solve each problem.

Michelle has 18 tickets.

She uses 9 of them.

How many tickets are left?

$$\begin{array}{r} 18 \\ -\ 9 \\ \hline 9 \end{array}$$

Jeff buys 14 nails.

He uses 6 of them.

How many are left?

There are 10 people on the train.

7 more get on.

How many people are on the train?

Jim has 13 pencils in his desk.

He takes 4 pencils out of his desk.

How many pencils are left in his desk?

Sally's house has 7 windows in it.

June's house has 9 windows in it.

How many windows do Sally's and June's houses have in all?

Perfect score: 5 My score: ______

NAME ____________

Lesson 8 Addition and Subtraction

Add or subtract.

If you get 9, color the part red.
If you get 14, color the part brown.

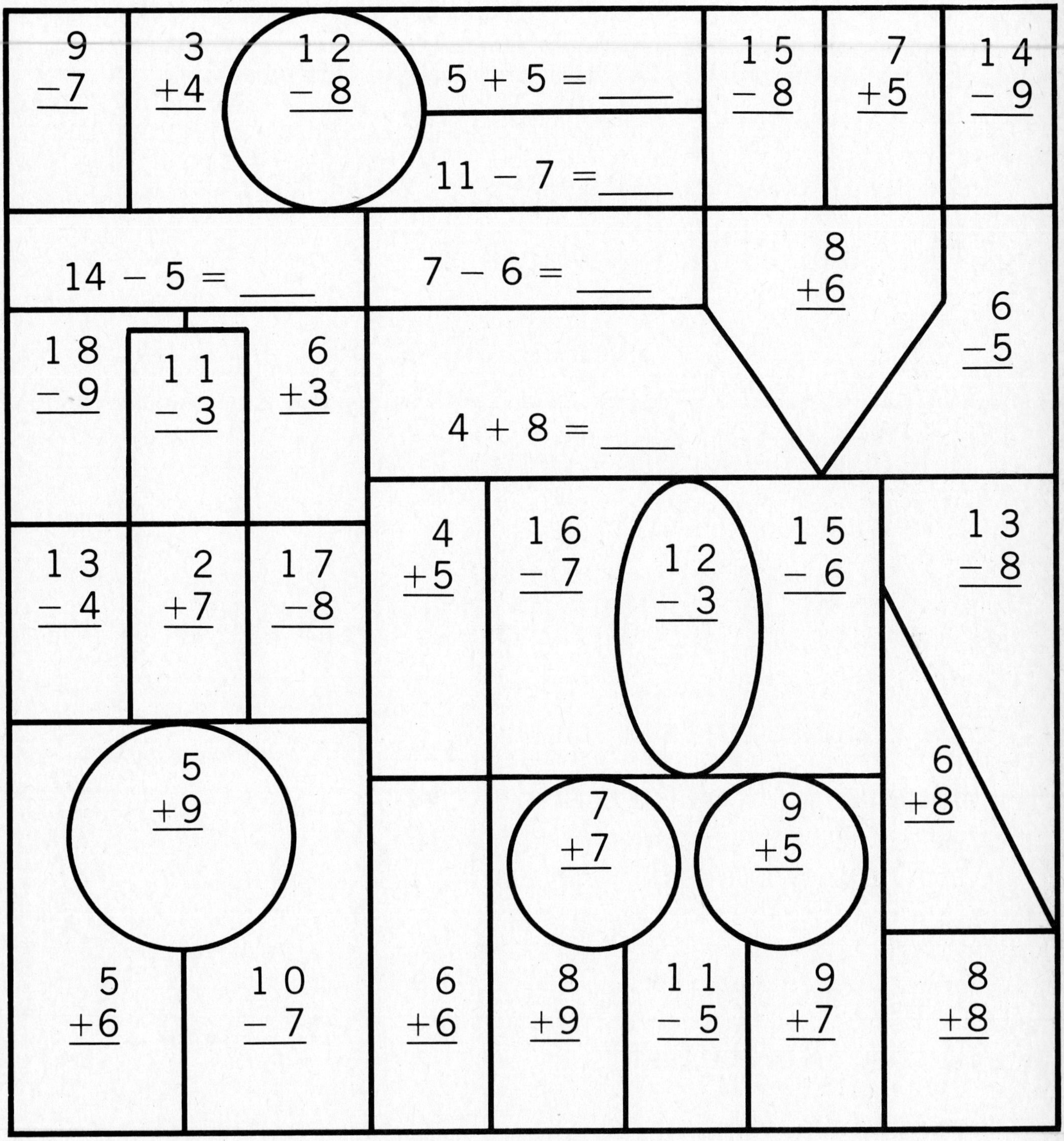

Perfect score: 35 My score: ____________

Problem Solving

Solve each problem.

Linda needed 17 balloons for a party.

Linda had 8 balloons at home.

How many more balloons did Linda need?

$$\begin{array}{r} 17 \\ -\ 8 \\ \hline 9 \end{array}$$

Jim had 9 white cowboy hats.

He also had 7 black cowboy hats.

How many cowboy hats did Jim have?

The office helper had 18 letters to write.

She wrote 9.

How many more letters did she have to write?

Dave read 8 books at school.

Jane read 7 books at school.

How many books did Dave and Jane read in all?

Craig had 16 bolts.

He used 8 of the bolts.

How many bolts did Craig have left?

Perfect score: 5 My score: ______

NAME ____________________

Chapter 3 Checkup

Add.

5	6	9	8	5	7
+8	+7	+5	+9	+6	+7

7	9	6	9	8	7
+6	+9	+9	+7	+8	+8

Subtract.

12	16	11	13	15	14
− 7	− 8	− 8	− 9	− 7	− 9

18	13	17	14	12	13
− 9	− 4	− 9	− 5	− 9	− 6

Solve each problem.

tomatoes on vine
tomatoes on ground
tomatoes in all

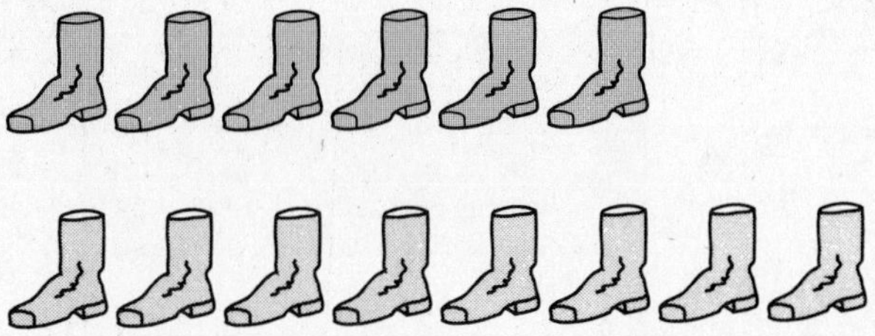

boots in all
gray boots
blue boots

Perfect score: 26 My score: ________

NAME ____________

PRE-TEST

Circle the fraction that tells how much is blue.

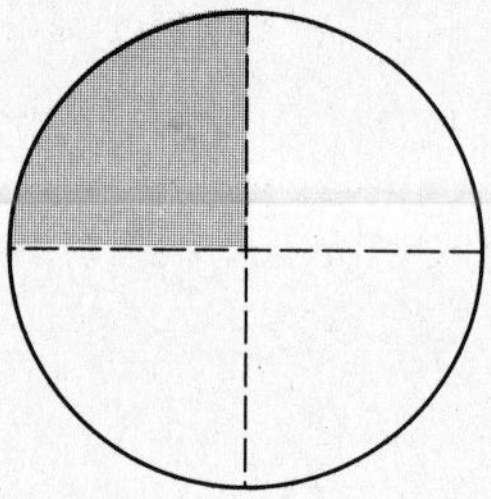

$\frac{1}{3}$ $\frac{1}{2}$ $\frac{1}{4}$

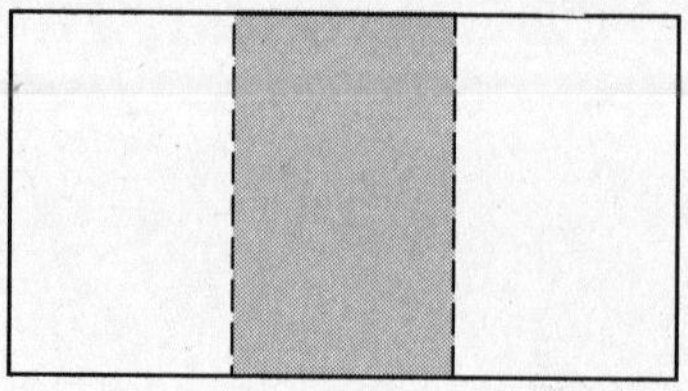

$\frac{1}{2}$ $\frac{1}{3}$ $\frac{1}{4}$

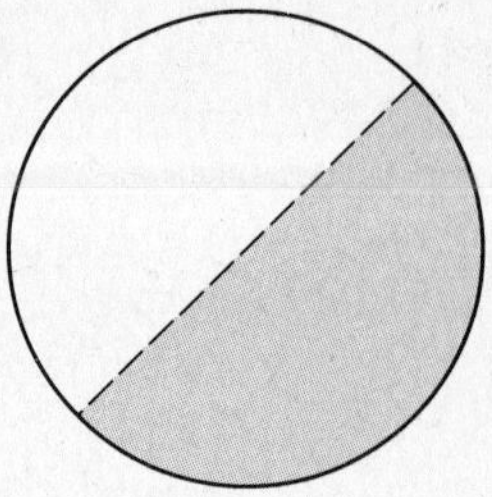

$\frac{1}{4}$ $\frac{1}{3}$ $\frac{1}{2}$

Write the time for each clock.

_____ o'clock

half past _____

_____ o'clock

Use a centimeter ruler. How long is each object?

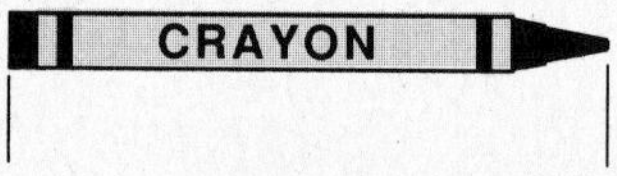

____ centimeters

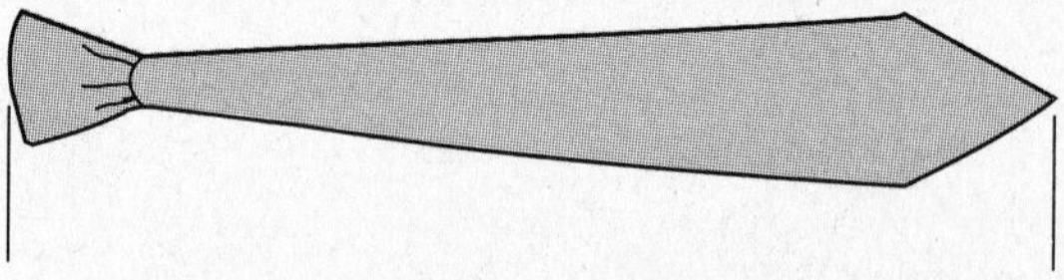

____ centimeters

Use an inch ruler. How long is each object?

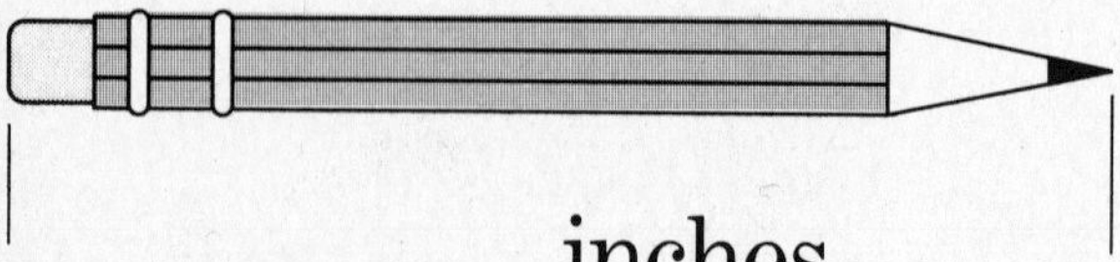

____ inches

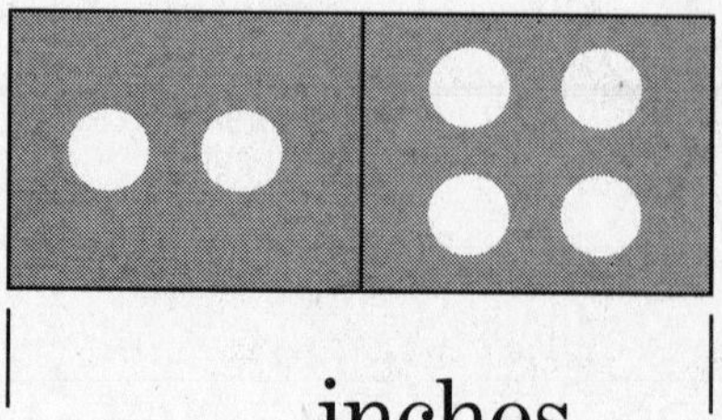

____ inches

Perfect score: 10 My score: ________

Lesson 1 One Half

NAME ____________________

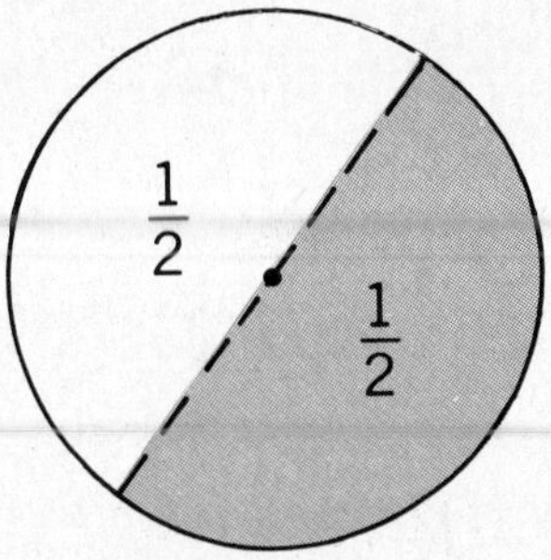

1 part is blue.

The 2 parts are the same size.

$\frac{1}{2}$ of the inside is blue.

Complete.

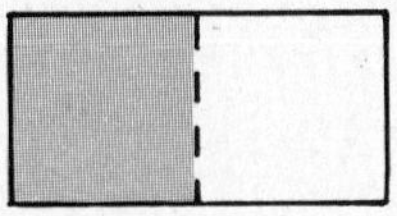

1 part is blue.

2 parts are the same size.

$\frac{1}{2}$ of the inside is blue.

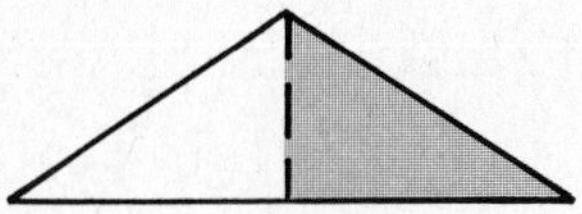

___ part is blue.

___ parts are the same size.

___ of the inside is blue.

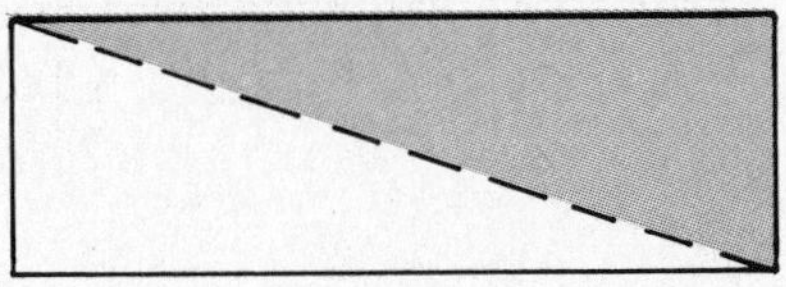

___ part is blue.

___ parts are the same size.

___ of the inside is blue.

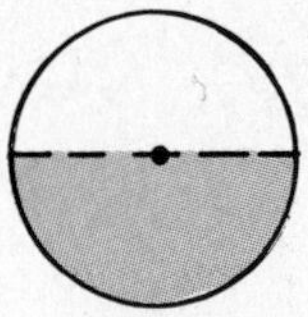

___ part is blue.

___ parts are the same size.

___ of the inside is blue.

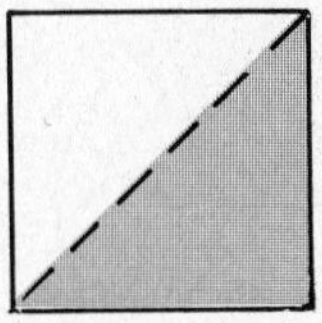

___ of the inside is blue.

___ of the inside is blue.

Perfect score: 14 My score: ________

Lesson 2 One Third

NAME ____________________

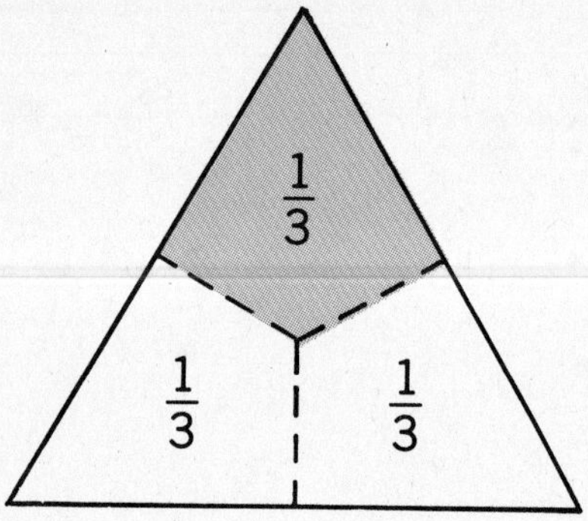

1 part is blue.

The 3 parts are the same size.

$\frac{1}{3}$ of the inside is blue.

Complete.

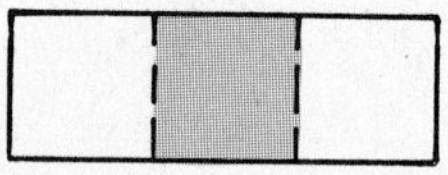

1 part is blue.

3 parts are the same size.

$\frac{1}{3}$ of the inside is blue.

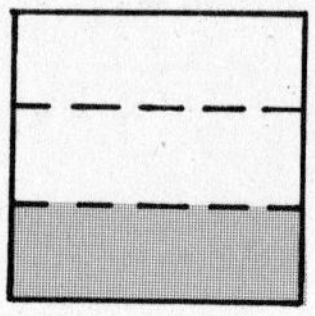

___ part is blue.

___ parts are the same size.

___ of the inside is blue.

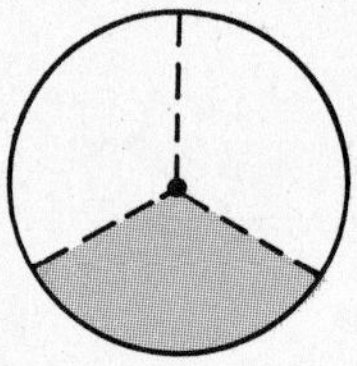

___ part is blue.

___ parts are the same size.

___ of the inside is blue.

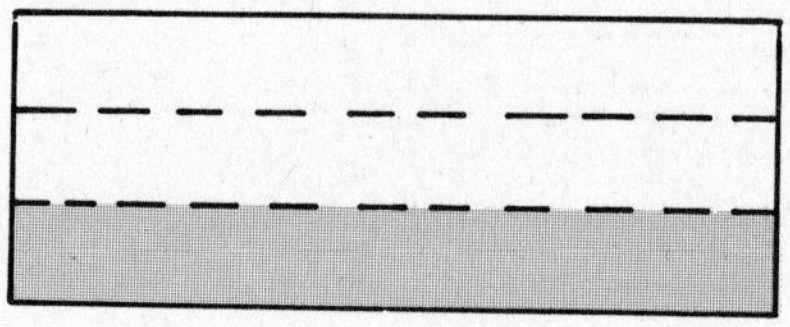

___ part is blue.

___ parts are the same size.

___ of the inside is blue.

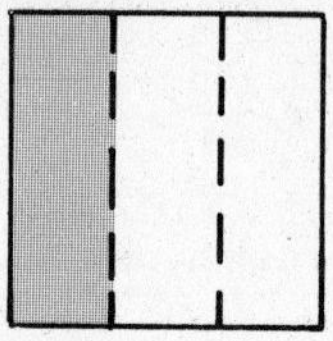

___ of the inside is blue.

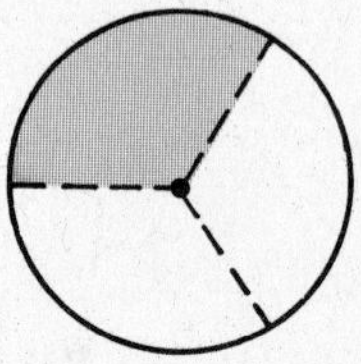

___ of the inside is blue.

Perfect score: 14 My score: ________

Lesson 3 One Fourth

NAME ____________________

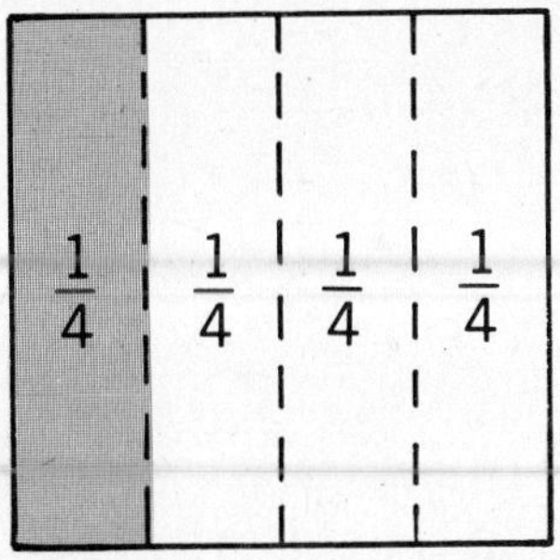

1 part is blue.

The 4 parts are the same size.

$\frac{1}{4}$ of the inside is blue.

Complete.

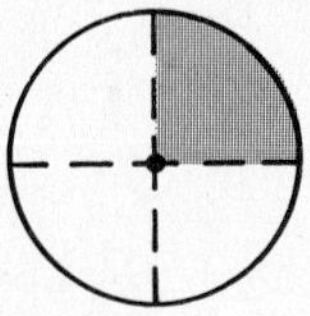

1 part is blue.

4 parts are the same size.

$\frac{1}{4}$ of the inside is blue.

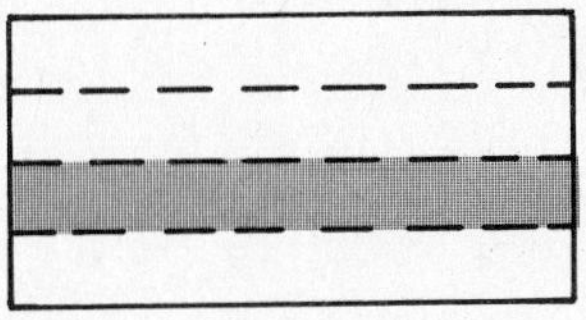

___ part is blue.

___ parts are the same size.

___ of the inside is blue.

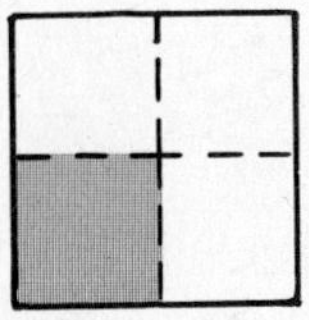

___ part is blue.

___ parts are the same size.

___ of the inside is blue.

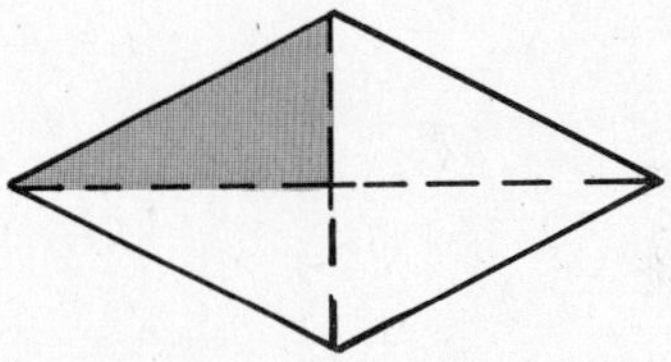

___ part is blue.

___ parts are the same size.

___ of the inside is blue.

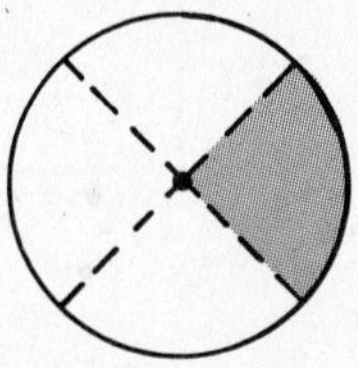

___ of the inside is blue.

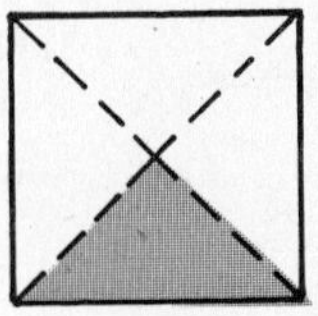

___ of the inside is blue.

Perfect score: 14 My score: ________

Fractions

Ring the fraction that tells how much is blue.

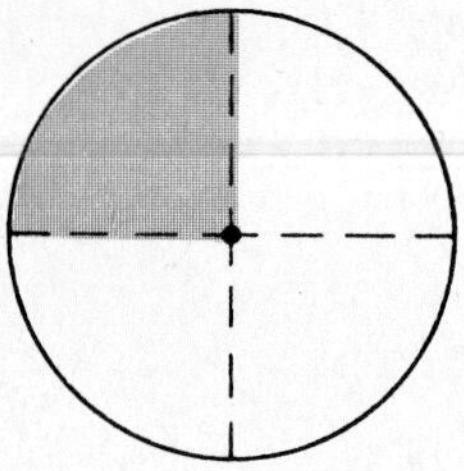

$\frac{1}{2}$ $\frac{1}{3}$ $\frac{1}{4}$

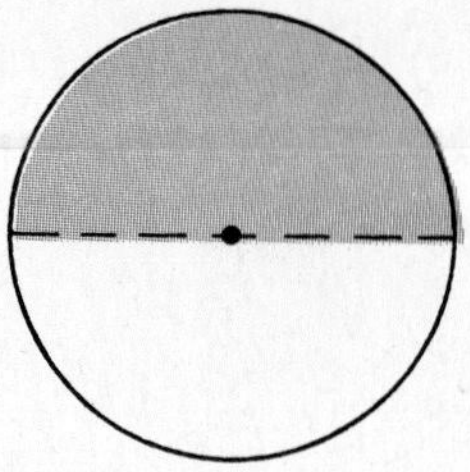

$\frac{1}{2}$ $\frac{1}{3}$ $\frac{1}{4}$

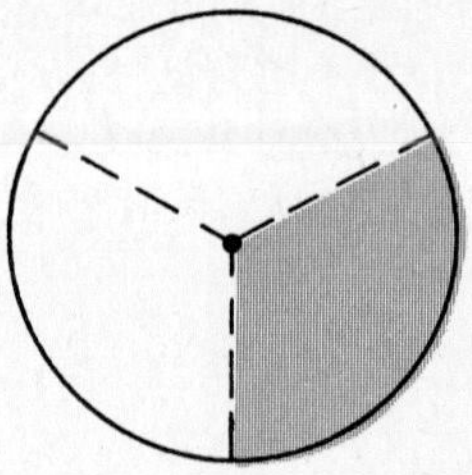

$\frac{1}{2}$ $\frac{1}{3}$ $\frac{1}{4}$

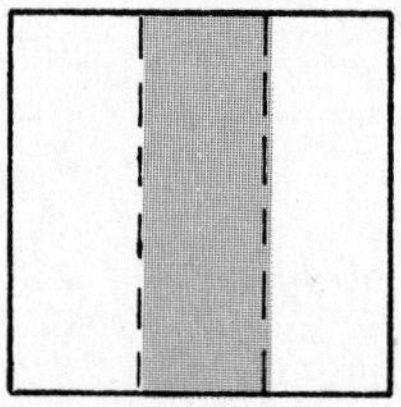

$\frac{1}{2}$ $\frac{1}{3}$ $\frac{1}{4}$

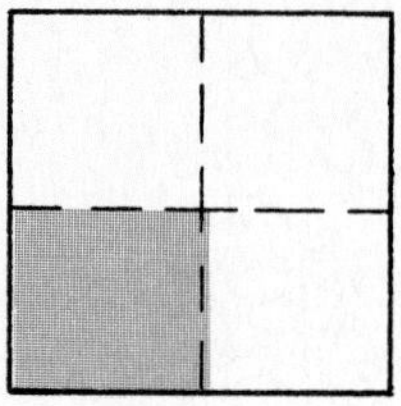

$\frac{1}{2}$ $\frac{1}{3}$ $\frac{1}{4}$

$\frac{1}{2}$ $\frac{1}{3}$ $\frac{1}{4}$

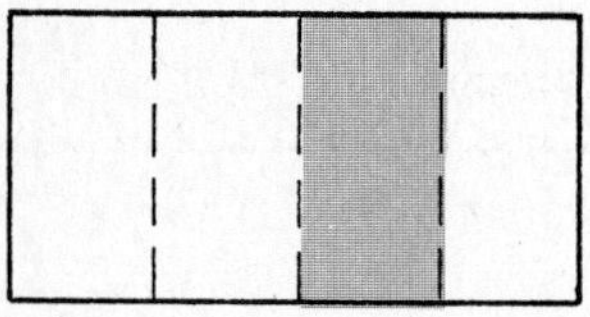

$\frac{1}{2}$ $\frac{1}{3}$ $\frac{1}{4}$

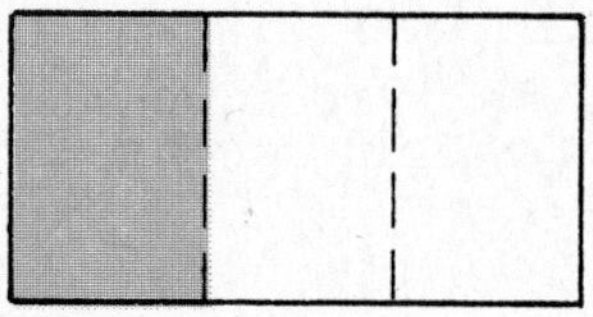

$\frac{1}{2}$ $\frac{1}{3}$ $\frac{1}{4}$

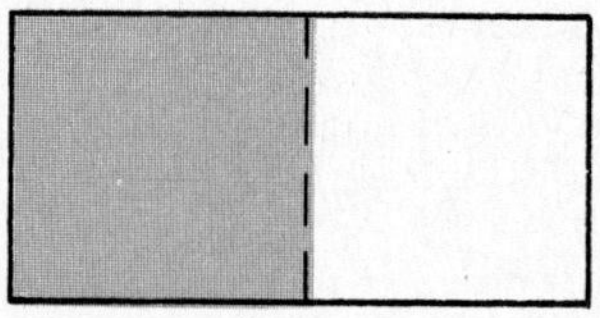

$\frac{1}{2}$ $\frac{1}{3}$ $\frac{1}{4}$

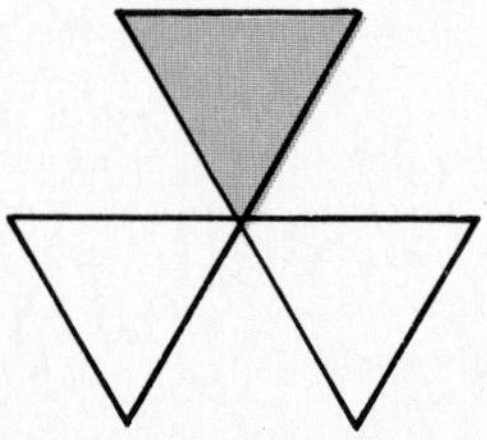

$\frac{1}{2}$ $\frac{1}{3}$ $\frac{1}{4}$

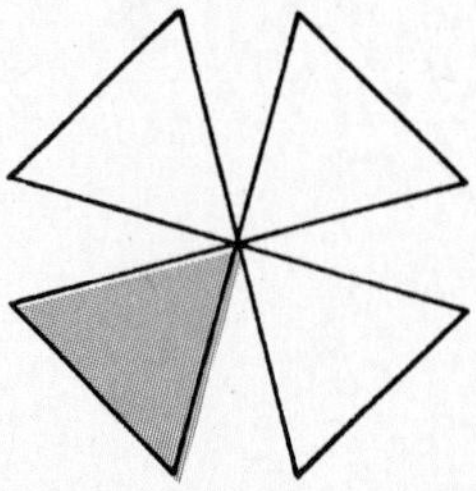

$\frac{1}{2}$ $\frac{1}{3}$ $\frac{1}{4}$

$\frac{1}{2}$ $\frac{1}{3}$ $\frac{1}{4}$

Perfect score: 12 My score: ________

NAME ____________________

Lesson 4 Time—Hour

8 o'clock

8:00

Both clocks show the same time.

Write the time for each clock.

4 o'clock

4 : 00

____ o'clock

____ : 00

____ o'clock

____ : 00

____ o'clock

____ : ____

____ o'clock

____ : ____

____ o'clock

____ : ____

____ o'clock

____ : ____

____ o'clock

____ : ____

____ o'clock

____ : ____

Perfect score: 18 My score: ____

Lesson 5 Time—Half Hour

NAME ______________________

2 o'clock
2:00

half past 2
2:30

3 o'clock
3:00

Write the time for each clock.

half past 3
3 : 30

half past ______
______ : 30

half past ______
______ : 30

half past ______
______ : ______

half past ______
______ : ______

half past ______
______ : ______

half past ______
______ : ______

half past ______
______ : ______

half past ______
______ : ______

Perfect score: 18 My score: ______

Lesson 6 Time

NAME ______________________

Show this time on this clock. Show this time on this clock.

Perfect score: 6 My score: ________

Problem Solving

Solve each problem.

The small hand is on the 3

The large hand is on the 12

The time is 3 o'clock.

The small hand is on the

The large hand is on the

The time is _____ o'clock.

The large hand is on the

The small hand is on the

The time is _____ o'clock.

The small hand is on the

The large hand is on the

The time is _____ o'clock.

The large hand is on the

The small hand is between _____ and _____.

The time is _____:_____.

Perfect score: 5 My score: _______

NAME ________________

Lesson 7 Calendar

OCTOBER

S	M	T	W	T	F	S
1	2	3	4	5	6	7
8	9	10	11	12	13	14
15	16	17	18	19	20	21
22	23	24	25	26	27	28
29	30	31				

Complete.

How many days are in October? ______

How many Saturdays are in October? ______

How many days are in 1 week? ______

How many days are in 2 weeks? ______

How many Tuesdays are in October? ______

What day of the week is the 26th? ______

Perfect score: 6 My score: ________

Calendar

JANUARY

S	M	T	W	T	F	S
1	2	3	4	5	6	7
8	9	10	11	12	13	14
15	16	17	18	19	20	21
22	23	24	25	26	27	28
29	30	31				

FEBRUARY

S	M	T	W	T	F	S
			1	2	3	4
5	6	7	8	9	10	11
12	13	14	15	16	17	18
19	20	21	22	23	24	25
26	27	28				

MARCH

S	M	T	W	T	F	S
			1	2	3	4
5	6	7	8	9	10	11
12	13	14	15	16	17	18
19	20	21	22	23	24	25
26	27	28	29	30	31	

APRIL

S	M	T	W	T	F	S
						1
2	3	4	5	6	7	8
9	10	11	12	13	14	15
16	17	18	19	20	21	22
23/30	24	25	26	27	28	29

MAY

S	M	T	W	T	F	S
	1	2	3	4	5	6
7	8	9	10	11	12	13
14	15	16	17	18	19	20
21	22	23	24	25	26	27
28	29	30	31			

JUNE

S	M	T	W	T	F	S
				1	2	3
4	5	6	7	8	9	10
11	12	13	14	15	16	17
18	19	20	21	22	23	24
25	26	27	28	29	30	

JULY

S	M	T	W	T	F	S
						1
2	3	4	5	6	7	8
9	10	11	12	13	14	15
16	17	18	19	20	21	22
23/30	24/31	25	26	27	28	29

AUGUST

S	M	T	W	T	F	S
		1	2	3	4	5
6	7	8	9	10	11	12
13	14	15	16	17	18	19
20	21	22	23	24	25	26
27	28	29	30	31		

SEPTEMBER

S	M	T	W	T	F	S
					1	2
3	4	5	6	7	8	9
10	11	12	13	14	15	16
17	18	19	20	21	22	23
24	25	26	27	28	29	30

OCTOBER

S	M	T	W	T	F	S
1	2	3	4	5	6	7
8	9	10	11	12	13	14
15	16	17	18	19	20	21
22	23	24	25	26	27	28
29	30	31				

NOVEMBER

S	M	T	W	T	F	S
			1	2	3	4
5	6	7	8	9	10	11
12	13	14	15	16	17	18
19	20	21	22	23	24	25
26	27	28	29	30		

DECEMBER

S	M	T	W	T	F	S
					1	2
3	4	5	6	7	8	9
10	11	12	13	14	15	16
17	18	19	20	21	22	23
24/31	25	26	27	28	29	30

Complete.

How many months are in 1 year? _____

How many months have exactly 30 days? _____

How many months have 31 days? _____

Which month has only 28 days? _____

How many months begin with the letter J? _____

How many months have 5 Saturdays? _____

Perfect score: 6 My score: _______

Lesson 8 Centimeter

NAME ____________________

1 centimeter

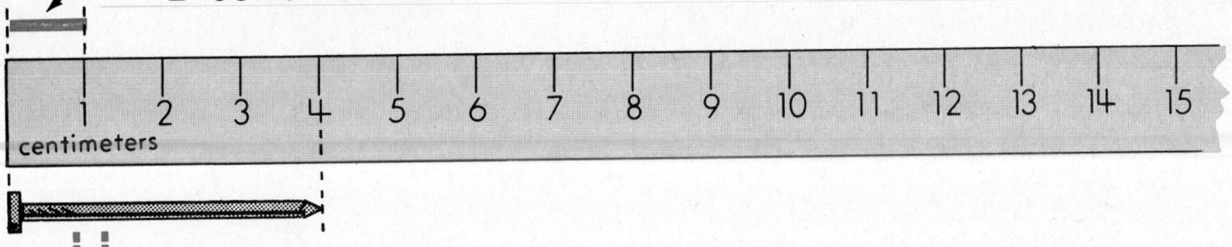

__4__ centimeters

How long is each object?

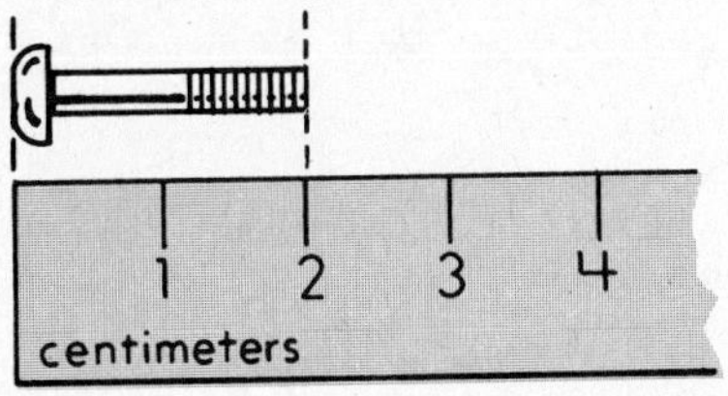

____ centimeters

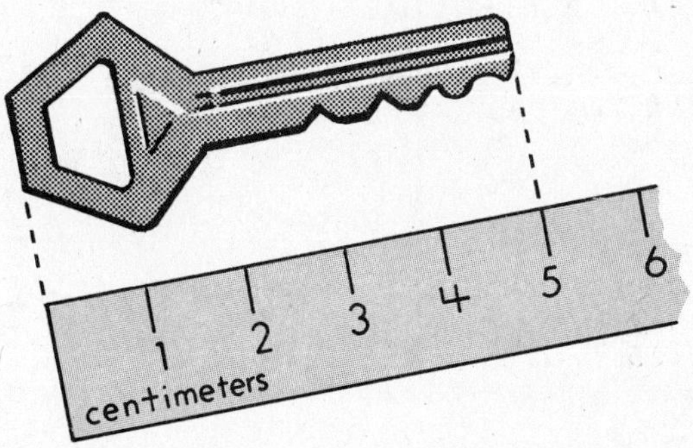

____ centimeters

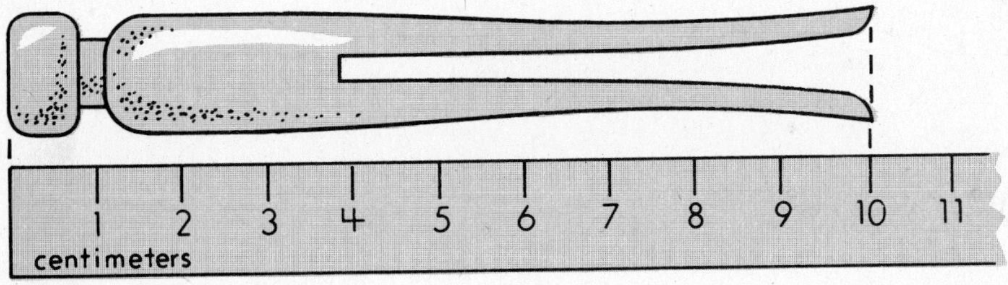

____ centimeters

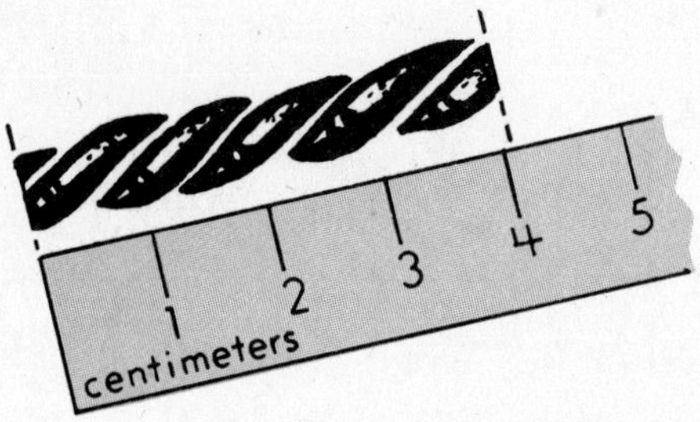

____ centimeters

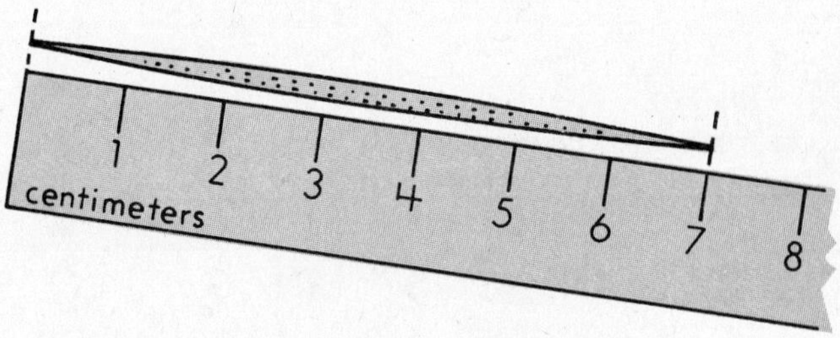

____ centimeters

Perfect score: 5 My score: ________

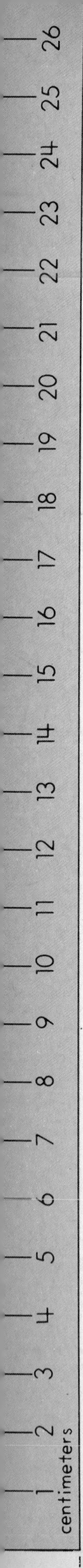

Centimeter

← Cut off this ruler.

How long is each object?

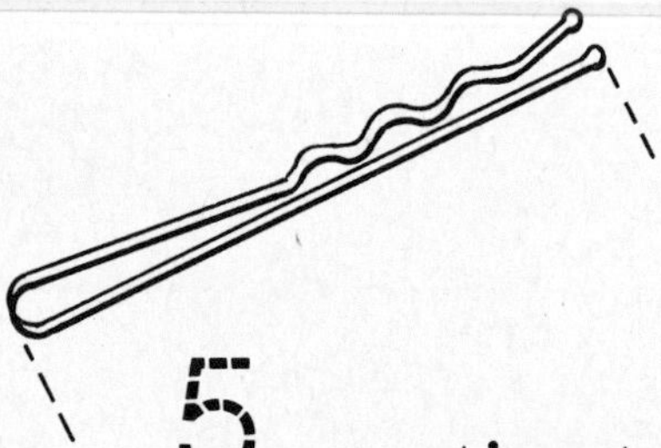

5 centimeters

____ centimeter

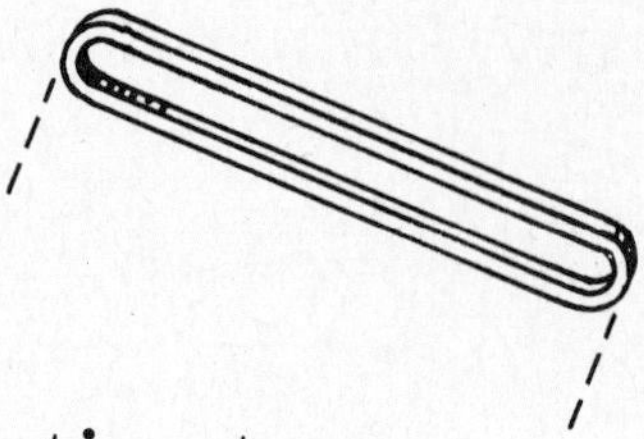

____ centimeters

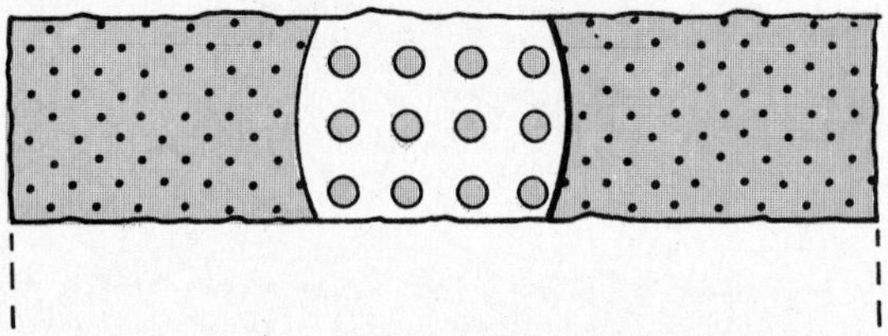

____ centimeters

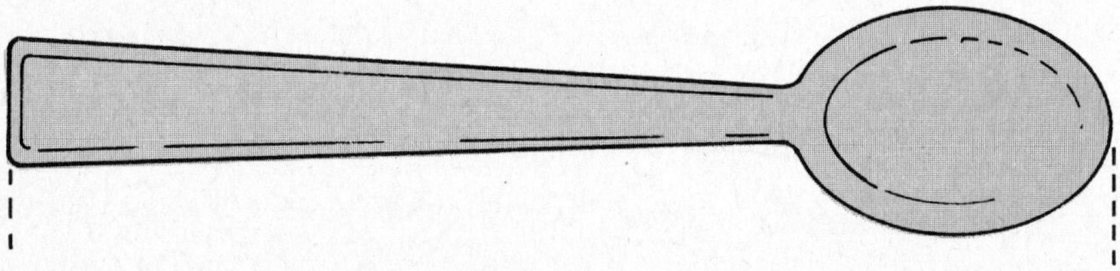

____ centimeters

____ centimeters

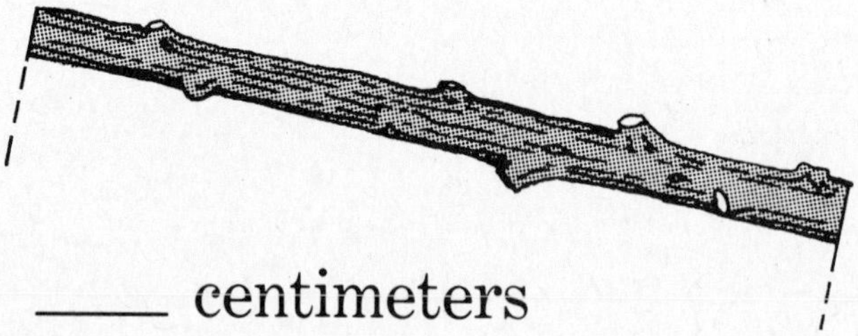

____ centimeters

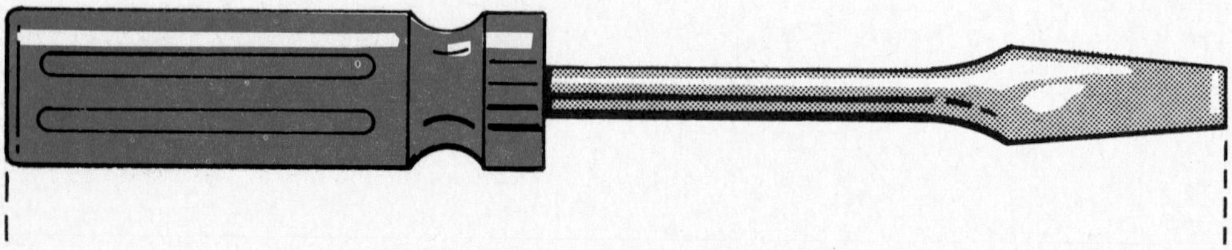

____ centimeters

Perfect score: 8 My score: ________

NAME ____________________

Lesson 9 Inch

1 inch

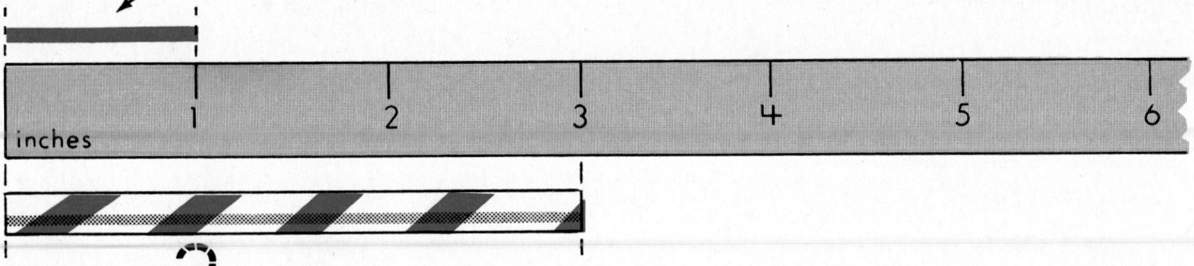

3 inches

How long is each object?

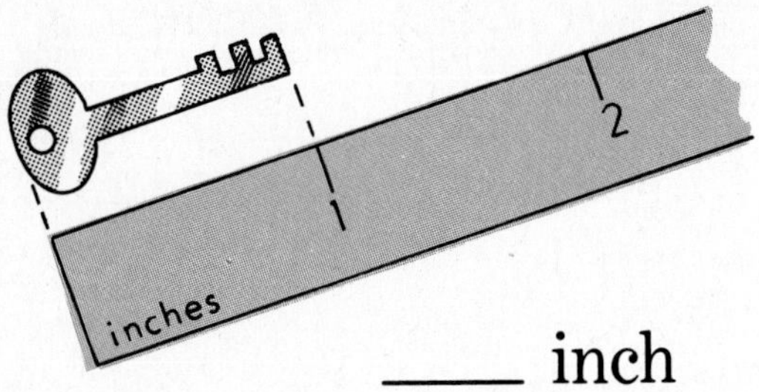

____ inch

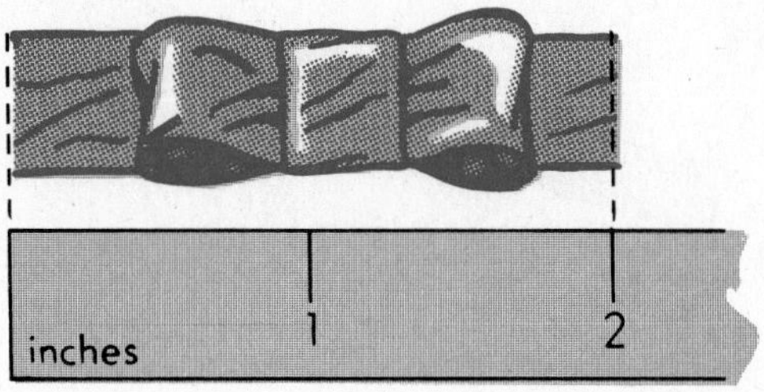

____ inches

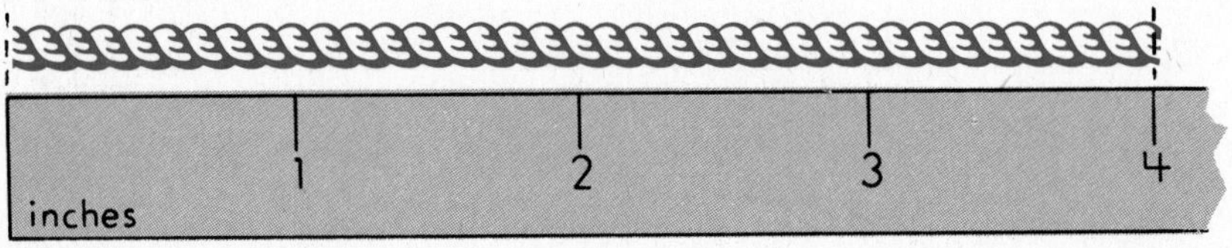

____ inches

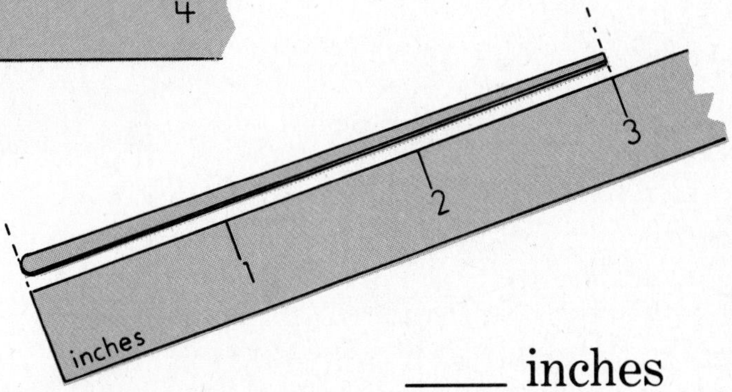

____ inches

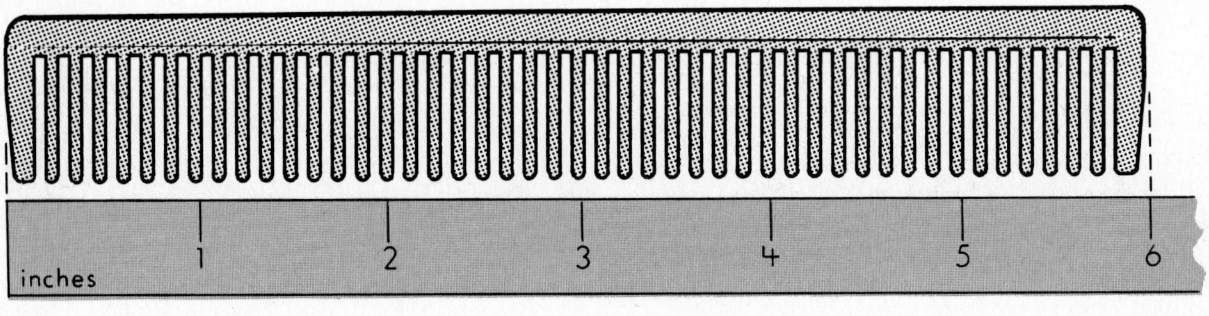

____ inches

Perfect score: 5 My score: ________

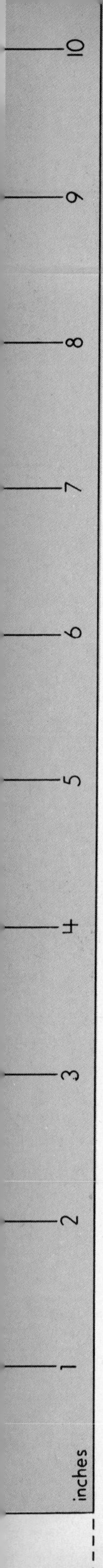

Inch

← Cut off this ruler.

How long is each object?

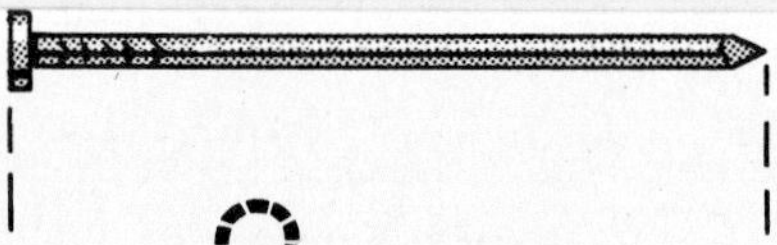

2 inches

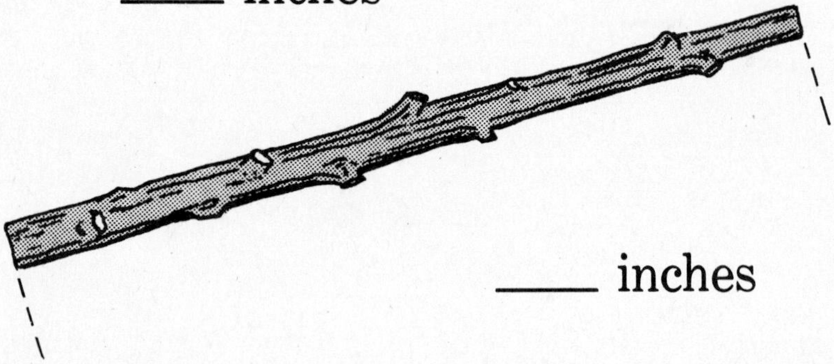

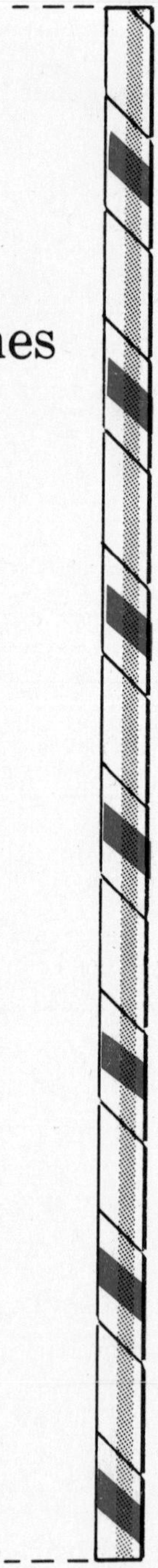

____ inches

____ inches

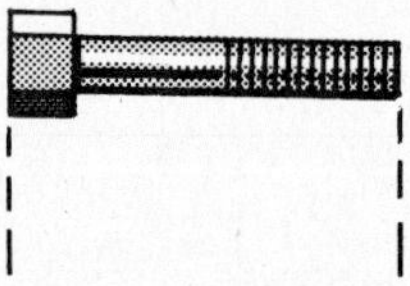

____ inch

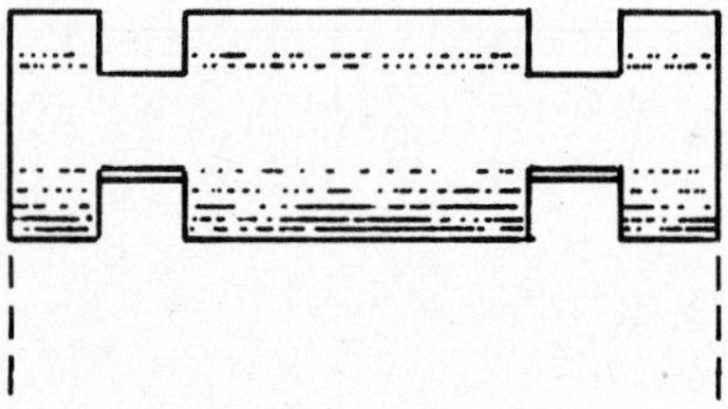

____ inches

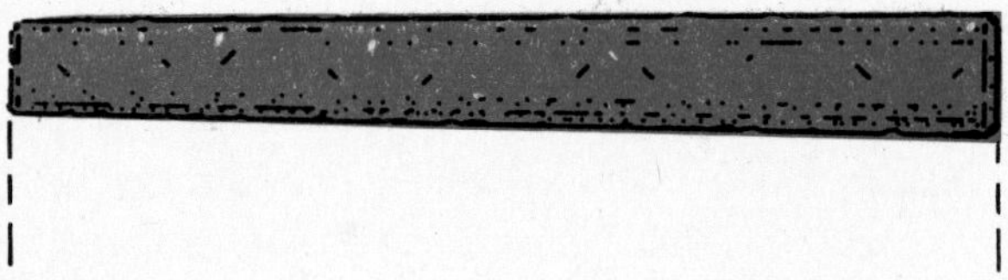

____ inches

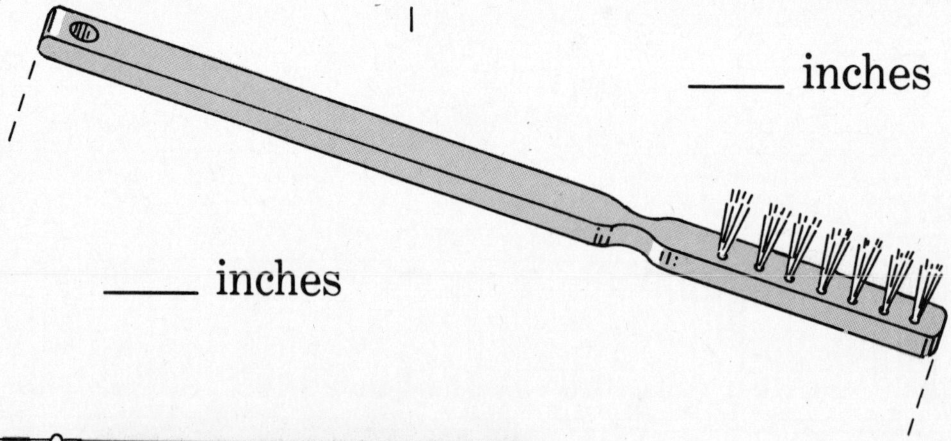

____ inches

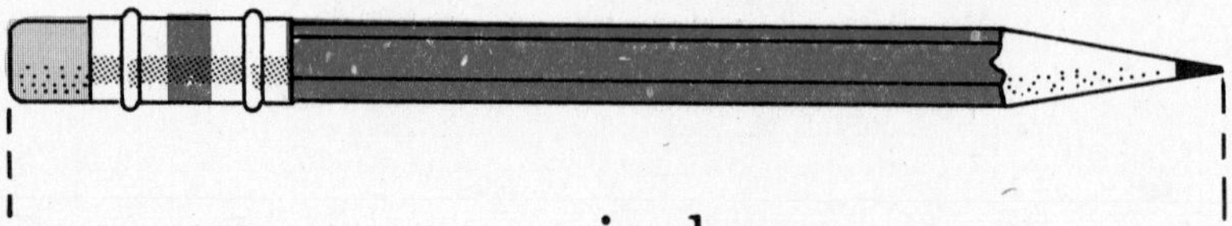

____ inches

Perfect score: 8 My score: ________

Chapter 4 Checkup

NAME ______________________

Use a centimeter ruler.

How long is each object?

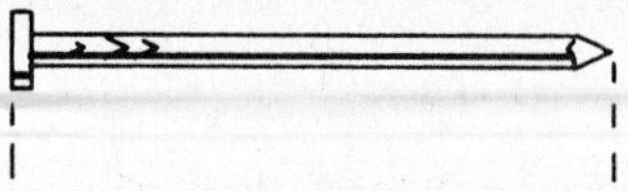

____ centimeters

____ centimeters

Ring the fraction that tells how much is blue.

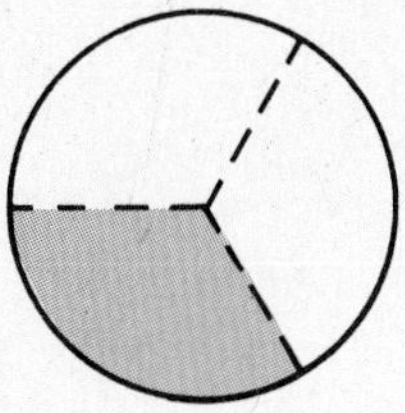

$\frac{1}{2}$ $\frac{1}{3}$ $\frac{1}{4}$

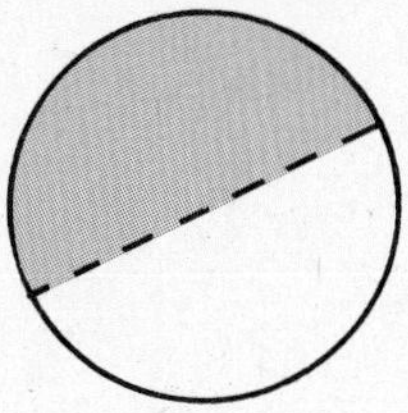

$\frac{1}{2}$ $\frac{1}{3}$ $\frac{1}{4}$

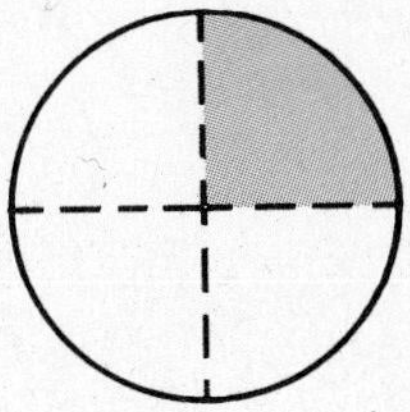

$\frac{1}{2}$ $\frac{1}{3}$ $\frac{1}{4}$

Use an inch ruler.

How long is each object?

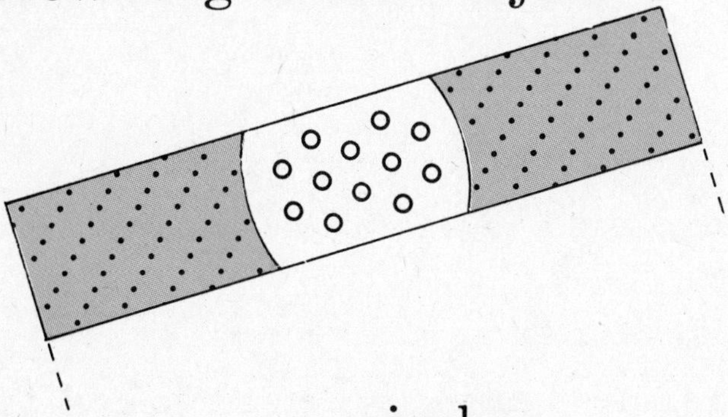

____ inches

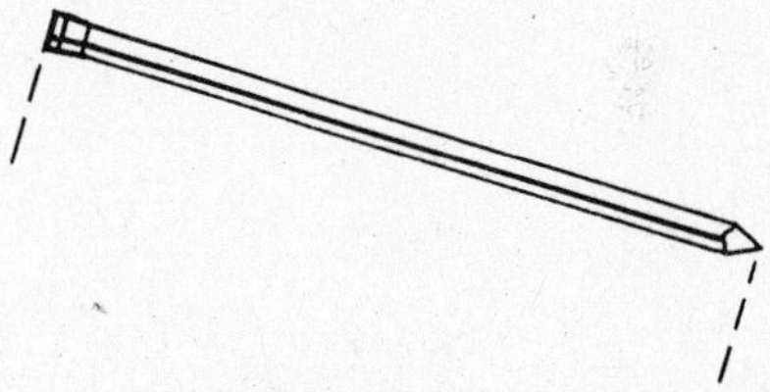

____ inches

Write the time for each clock.

______:______

______:______

______:______

Perfect score: 10 My score: ______

PRE-TEST

Add.

20 +30	30 +40	60 +30	70 +10	40 +10
55 +23	60 +15	70 +12	82 +15	93 + 3
4 2 +1	2 2 +2	20 10 +30	40 20 +10	30 40 +20

Subtract.

40 −10	60 −20	70 −40	30 −20	80 −50
85 −24	76 −23	99 −33	65 −14	53 −20

Perfect score: 25 My score: __________

NAME ____________________

Lesson 1 Addition and Subtraction Review

Add.

9 + 8	6 + 6	7 + 9	5 + 7	9 + 9	4 + 8
7 + 6	6 + 9	8 + 6	7 + 7	5 + 8	8 + 2
9 + 4	7 + 8	5 + 5	9 + 1	3 + 9	5 + 6

Subtract.

18 − 9	11 − 9	10 − 5	12 − 4	13 − 7	14 − 9
10 − 6	12 − 7	13 − 5	11 − 3	15 − 8	10 − 9
14 − 7	11 − 6	15 − 7	17 − 9	12 − 8	13 − 4

Perfect score: 36 My score: ________

Ring each name for the number in the ◯.

(11)

4 + 8
5 + 6
9 + 2
4 + 7
6 + 6
8 + 3

(16)

5 + 7
6 + 9
8 + 7
7 + 9
9 + 7
8 + 8

(15)

7 + 8
7 + 7
8 + 7
6 + 9
5 + 9
9 + 6

(13)

8 + 5
6 + 8
7 + 6
9 + 4
9 + 5
6 + 7
4 + 8

(7)

13 − 6
17 − 8
15 − 8
16 − 9
14 − 7
14 − 6

(8)

17 − 9
15 − 7
10 − 6
13 − 5
12 − 4
11 − 7
11 − 3

(6)

13 − 7
14 − 8
15 − 6
16 − 7
12 − 6
12 − 8

(9)

17 − 9
13 − 4
16 − 7
11 − 5
15 − 7
12 − 8
18 − 9

Perfect score: 30 My score: ______

NAME ______________________

Lesson 2 Adding Tens

3 tens +4 tens 7 tens	30 +40 70	6 tens +2 tens 8 tens	60 +20 80

Add.

2 tens +4 tens tens	20 +40	5 tens +3 tens tens	50 +30

20 +20	10 +50	40 +20	30 +40	50 +30
30 +20	60 +10	20 +50	70 +10	10 +10
10 +20	40 +40	80 +10	60 +30	20 +60
70 +20	40 +10	30 +10	50 +40	30 +30

Perfect score: 24 My score: ________

Solve each problem.

There are 20 men in the plane.

30 women get in the plane.

How many men and women are in the plane?

$$\begin{array}{r} 20 \\ +30 \\ \hline \end{array}$$

Jill buys 10 apples.

Carol buys 20 apples.

How many apples in all?

There are 30 ears of corn in one pile.

There are 50 ears of corn in another pile.

How many ears of corn in all?

Henry cut 40 pieces of wood.

Art cut 20 pieces of wood.

How many pieces of wood were cut?

Adolpho had 60 baseball cards.

Maria had 30 baseball cards.

How many baseball cards in all?

Perfect score: 5 My score: ______

NAME ____________________

Lesson 3 Addition

Join the pennies.
Add the ones.

$$\begin{array}{r} 34 \\ +23 \\ \hline 7 \end{array}$$

Join the dimes.
Add the tens.

$$\begin{array}{r} 34 \\ +23 \\ \hline 57 \end{array}$$

Add.

$\begin{array}{r} 23 \\ +14 \\ \hline 37 \end{array}$		$\begin{array}{r} 55 \\ +\ 2 \\ \hline \end{array}$	$\begin{array}{r} 70 \\ +23 \\ \hline \end{array}$	$\begin{array}{r} 60 \\ +13 \\ \hline \end{array}$
$\begin{array}{r} 43 \\ +52 \\ \hline \end{array}$	$\begin{array}{r} 36 \\ +21 \\ \hline \end{array}$	$\begin{array}{r} 45 \\ +13 \\ \hline \end{array}$	$\begin{array}{r} 83 \\ +12 \\ \hline \end{array}$	$\begin{array}{r} 26 \\ +43 \\ \hline \end{array}$
$\begin{array}{r} 53 \\ +42 \\ \hline \end{array}$	$\begin{array}{r} 38 \\ +31 \\ \hline \end{array}$	$\begin{array}{r} 81 \\ +\ 3 \\ \hline \end{array}$	$\begin{array}{r} 33 \\ +53 \\ \hline \end{array}$	$\begin{array}{r} 75 \\ +22 \\ \hline \end{array}$
$\begin{array}{r} 71 \\ +27 \\ \hline \end{array}$	$\begin{array}{r} 62 \\ +14 \\ \hline \end{array}$	$\begin{array}{r} 67 \\ +22 \\ \hline \end{array}$	$\begin{array}{r} 43 \\ +46 \\ \hline \end{array}$	$\begin{array}{r} 34 \\ +30 \\ \hline \end{array}$
$\begin{array}{r} 31 \\ +50 \\ \hline \end{array}$	$\begin{array}{r} 60 \\ +32 \\ \hline \end{array}$	$\begin{array}{r} 54 \\ +20 \\ \hline \end{array}$	$\begin{array}{r} 47 \\ +30 \\ \hline \end{array}$	$\begin{array}{r} 40 \\ +40 \\ \hline \end{array}$

(In the example 23 + 14 = 37: the 7 — Add the ones. The 3 — Add the tens.)

Perfect score: 24 My score: ________

Problem Solving

Solve each problem.

Pablo sees 25  .

Paco sees 34  .

How many  in all?

$$\begin{array}{r} 25 \\ +\,34 \\ \hline \end{array}$$

Payne bought 14  .

Paul bought 12  .

How many  in all?

Lewis drinks 21 

a week.

Lee drinks 28 

a week.

How many 

do Lewis and Lee drink in 1 week?

June has 31  .

Melody has 24  .

How many  in all?

Georgia peeled 41 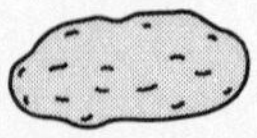 .

Lillian peeled 37 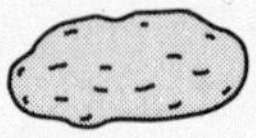 .

How many 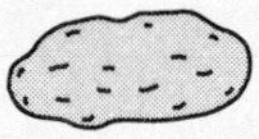 did Georgia and Lillian peel?

Perfect score: 5 My score: ________

NAME ____________________

Lesson 4 Addition (2 digit)

Add.

$\begin{array}{r} 45 \\ +32 \\ \hline 77 \end{array}$	$\begin{array}{r} 52 \\ +24 \\ \hline 76 \end{array}$	$\begin{array}{r} 40 \\ +10 \\ \hline \end{array}$	$\begin{array}{r} 22 \\ +22 \\ \hline \end{array}$	$\begin{array}{r} 65 \\ +13 \\ \hline \end{array}$
$\begin{array}{r} 14 \\ +51 \\ \hline \end{array}$	$\begin{array}{r} 18 \\ +41 \\ \hline \end{array}$	$\begin{array}{r} 63 \\ +31 \\ \hline \end{array}$	$\begin{array}{r} 34 \\ +51 \\ \hline \end{array}$	$\begin{array}{r} 46 \\ +32 \\ \hline \end{array}$
$\begin{array}{r} 23 \\ +54 \\ \hline \end{array}$	$\begin{array}{r} 44 \\ +42 \\ \hline \end{array}$	$\begin{array}{r} 62 \\ +35 \\ \hline \end{array}$	$\begin{array}{r} 73 \\ +25 \\ \hline \end{array}$	$\begin{array}{r} 80 \\ +15 \\ \hline \end{array}$
$\begin{array}{r} 64 \\ +15 \\ \hline \end{array}$	$\begin{array}{r} 15 \\ +22 \\ \hline \end{array}$	$\begin{array}{r} 33 \\ +33 \\ \hline \end{array}$	$\begin{array}{r} 82 \\ +17 \\ \hline \end{array}$	$\begin{array}{r} 71 \\ +25 \\ \hline \end{array}$
$\begin{array}{r} 26 \\ +33 \\ \hline \end{array}$	$\begin{array}{r} 18 \\ +31 \\ \hline \end{array}$	$\begin{array}{r} 43 \\ +12 \\ \hline \end{array}$	$\begin{array}{r} 24 \\ +24 \\ \hline \end{array}$	$\begin{array}{r} 55 \\ +23 \\ \hline \end{array}$
$\begin{array}{r} 72 \\ +24 \\ \hline \end{array}$	$\begin{array}{r} 66 \\ +32 \\ \hline \end{array}$	$\begin{array}{r} 54 \\ +11 \\ \hline \end{array}$	$\begin{array}{r} 11 \\ +11 \\ \hline \end{array}$	$\begin{array}{r} 25 \\ +24 \\ \hline \end{array}$

Perfect score: 30 My score: ________

Problem Solving

Ken has	Jill has	Pam has	Rod has

25¢	26¢	20¢	32¢

Complete.

Who has the most money? ____________

Who has the least money? ____________

Solve each problem.

Ken has	25 ¢	Pam has	20 ¢
Pam has	+ 20 ¢	Rod has	+ 32 ¢
Ken and Pam have	45 ¢	Pam and Rod have	¢
Jill has	¢	Rod has	¢
Pam has	+ ¢	Jill has	+ ¢
Jill and Pam have	¢	Rod and Jill have	¢
Ken has	¢	Pam has	¢
Rod has	+ ¢	Ken has	+ ¢
Ken and Rod have	¢	Pam and Ken have	¢

Perfect score: 8 My score: ________

NAME ____________________

Lesson 5 Subtracting Tens

6 tens	6 0	8 tens	8 0
−3 tens	−3 0	−2 tens	−2 0
3 tens	3 0	6 tens	60

Subtract.

7 tens	7 0	4 tens	4 0
−5 tens	−5 0	−2 tens	−2 0
tens		tens	

5 0	6 0	2 0	8 0	4 0
−3 0	−2 0	−1 0	−4 0	−4 0

9 0	8 0	7 0	3 0	5 0
−5 0	−2 0	−3 0	−2 0	−4 0

6 0	4 0	8 0	9 0	7 0
−3 0	−1 0	−3 0	−2 0	−5 0

8 0	9 0	7 0	6 0	5 0
−7 0	−8 0	−4 0	−4 0	−2 0

Perfect score: 24 My score: ________

Solve each problem.

Mr. Cobb counts 70 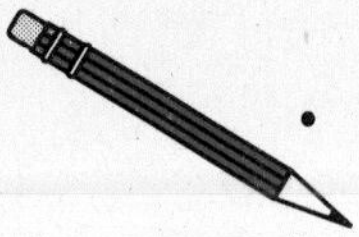 .
He sells 30 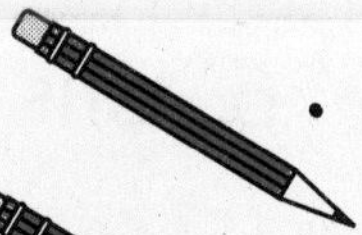 .
How many  are left?

$$\begin{array}{r} 70 \\ -\,30 \\ \hline 40 \end{array}$$

Keith has 20 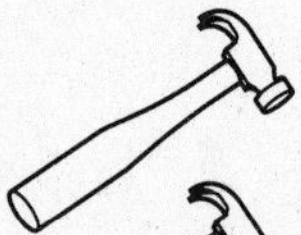 .
Leon has 10 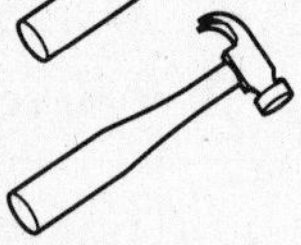 .
How many more  does Keith have than Leon?

Tina plants 60  .
Melody plants 30  .
How many more  did Tina plant than Melody?

Link has 80  .
Ellen has 50  .
How many more  does Link have than Ellen?

Jack hits 40  .
Harold hits 30  .
How many more  does Jack hit than Harold?

Perfect score: 5 My score: ________

Lesson 6 Subtraction (2 digit)

NAME ______________________

Take away 1 penny. Subtract the ones.	Take away 2 dimes. Subtract the tens.
$\begin{array}{r} 53 \\ -21 \\ \hline 2 \end{array}$	$\begin{array}{r} 53 \\ -21 \\ \hline 32 \end{array}$

Subtract.

$\begin{array}{r} 79 \\ -\ 6 \\ \hline 73 \end{array}$		$\begin{array}{r} 82 \\ -52 \\ \hline 30 \end{array}$	$\begin{array}{r} 65 \\ -24 \\ \hline \end{array}$	$\begin{array}{r} 56 \\ -26 \\ \hline \end{array}$

In 73, the 3 is labelled "Subtract the ones." and the 7 is labelled "Subtract the tens."

$\begin{array}{r} 87 \\ -23 \\ \hline \end{array}$	$\begin{array}{r} 36 \\ -20 \\ \hline \end{array}$	$\begin{array}{r} 94 \\ -\ 1 \\ \hline \end{array}$	$\begin{array}{r} 58 \\ -17 \\ \hline \end{array}$	$\begin{array}{r} 65 \\ -51 \\ \hline \end{array}$
$\begin{array}{r} 57 \\ -10 \\ \hline \end{array}$	$\begin{array}{r} 89 \\ -64 \\ \hline \end{array}$	$\begin{array}{r} 46 \\ -\ 3 \\ \hline \end{array}$	$\begin{array}{r} 75 \\ -15 \\ \hline \end{array}$	$\begin{array}{r} 37 \\ -24 \\ \hline \end{array}$
$\begin{array}{r} 46 \\ -34 \\ \hline \end{array}$	$\begin{array}{r} 78 \\ -68 \\ \hline \end{array}$	$\begin{array}{r} 29 \\ -\ 2 \\ \hline \end{array}$	$\begin{array}{r} 85 \\ -43 \\ \hline \end{array}$	$\begin{array}{r} 78 \\ -21 \\ \hline \end{array}$
$\begin{array}{r} 79 \\ -61 \\ \hline \end{array}$	$\begin{array}{r} 97 \\ -65 \\ \hline \end{array}$	$\begin{array}{r} 84 \\ -\ 2 \\ \hline \end{array}$	$\begin{array}{r} 65 \\ -22 \\ \hline \end{array}$	$\begin{array}{r} 99 \\ -37 \\ \hline \end{array}$

Perfect score: 24 My score: ________

Solve each problem.

Maria has	Pedro has	Madra has	Leroy has

45¢	42¢	65¢	32¢

Solve each problem.

Madra has 65¢	Maria has ____¢
Pedro has − 42¢	Pedro has − ____¢
Madra has this much more 23¢	Maria has this much more. ____¢
Pedro has ____¢	Madra has ____¢
Leroy has − ____¢	Leroy has − ____¢
Pedro has this much more. ____¢	Madra has this much more. ____¢
Madra has ____¢	Maria has ____¢
Maria has − ____¢	Leroy has − ____¢
Madra has this much more. ____¢	Maria has this much more. ____¢

Perfect score: 6 My score: ________

NAME ______________________

Lesson 7 Adding Three Numbers

Add the ones.	Add the tens.
$\begin{array}{r} 12 \\ 53 \\ +24 \\ \hline 9 \end{array}$ $\quad \begin{array}{r} 5 \\ +4 \\ \hline \end{array}$	$\begin{array}{r} 60 \\ +20 \\ \hline \end{array}$ $\quad \begin{array}{r} 12 \\ 53 \\ +24 \\ \hline 89 \end{array}$

Add.

$\begin{array}{r} 1 \\ 6 \\ +1 \\ \hline 8 \end{array}$ $\quad \begin{array}{r} 2 \\ 4 \\ +2 \\ \hline \end{array}$ $\quad \begin{array}{r} 3 \\ 5 \\ +0 \\ \hline \end{array}$ $\quad \begin{array}{r} 4 \\ 1 \\ +4 \\ \hline \end{array}$ $\quad \begin{array}{r} 2 \\ 2 \\ +5 \\ \hline \end{array}$ $\quad \begin{array}{r} 3 \\ 3 \\ +3 \\ \hline \end{array}$

$\begin{array}{r} 30 \\ 10 \\ +10 \\ \hline 50 \end{array}$ $\quad \begin{array}{r} 20 \\ 30 \\ +10 \\ \hline \end{array}$ $\quad \begin{array}{r} 20 \\ 20 \\ +20 \\ \hline \end{array}$ $\quad \begin{array}{r} 30 \\ 20 \\ +0 \\ \hline \end{array}$ $\quad \begin{array}{r} 40 \\ 30 \\ +10 \\ \hline \end{array}$

$\begin{array}{r} 31 \\ 16 \\ +11 \\ \hline 58 \end{array}$ $\quad \begin{array}{r} 14 \\ 10 \\ +11 \\ \hline \end{array}$ $\quad \begin{array}{r} 66 \\ 20 \\ +13 \\ \hline \end{array}$ $\quad \begin{array}{r} 15 \\ 51 \\ +1 \\ \hline \end{array}$ $\quad \begin{array}{r} 41 \\ 14 \\ +12 \\ \hline \end{array}$

$\begin{array}{r} 33 \\ 21 \\ +23 \\ \hline \end{array}$ $\quad \begin{array}{r} 31 \\ 12 \\ +51 \\ \hline \end{array}$ $\quad \begin{array}{r} 54 \\ 12 \\ +21 \\ \hline \end{array}$ $\quad \begin{array}{r} 71 \\ 17 \\ +1 \\ \hline \end{array}$ $\quad \begin{array}{r} 32 \\ 21 \\ +32 \\ \hline \end{array}$

Perfect score: 21 My score: ________

Why did the bird fly south?

A	F	I	K	L	O	R	S	T	W
7	9	35	39	47	58	59	68	86	88

Add. Write the letter for each answer.

12	43	30	3	25
12	22	24	2	31
+11	+21	+34	+2	+12
35				
I				

51	16	31	3	1	13
24	20	16	3	2	24
+11	+22	+11	+3	+4	+22

63	30	51	3	14	13
10	17	26	3	23	11
+13	+11	+11	+1	+10	+15

Perfect score: 34 My score: ________

NAME ____________________

Lesson 8 Money

half dollar

50¢

50¢

50¢

Tell how many cents there are.

50¢
+25¢
75¢

50¢
+30¢
___¢

___¢
+ ___¢
___¢

___¢
+ ___¢
___¢

50¢
25¢
+10¢
___¢

___¢
___¢
+ ___¢
___¢

Perfect score: 6 My score: ______

Problem Solving

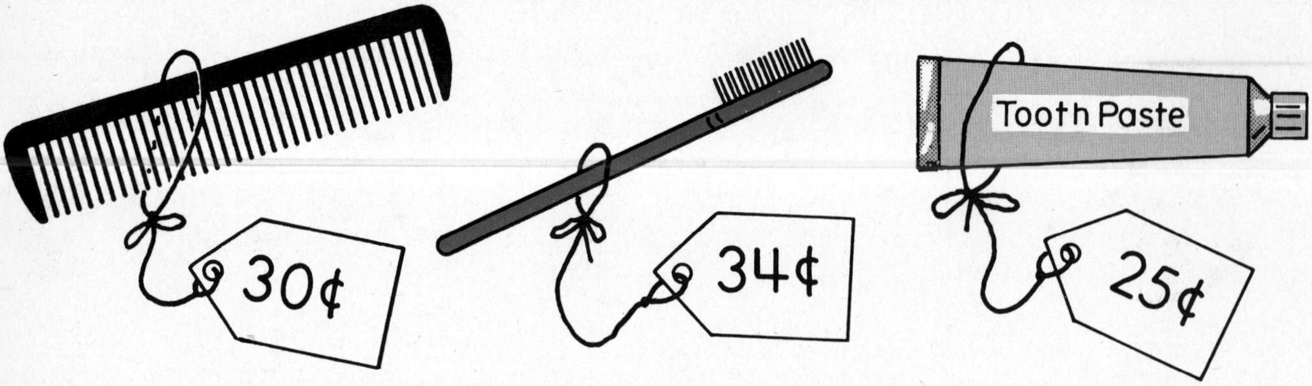

Solve each problem.

You buy a  30¢
and a . +34¢
You spent ¢

You have 5 0¢
You buy a . −30¢
You have left ¢

You buy a  ¢
and . + ¢
You spent ¢

You have 8 9¢
You buy a . − ¢
You have left ¢

You buy a  ¢
and . + ¢
You spent ¢

You have 9 7¢
You buy a . − ¢
You have left ¢

Perfect score: 6 My score: ______

NAME ______________________

Lesson 9 Addition and Subtraction

Add.

45 + 22	53 + 34	18 + 21	40 + 30	62 + 16	76 + 23
32 + 16	27 + 40	50 + 20	92 + 6	42 + 37	51 + 24
11 + 14 + 10	40 + 12 + 34	20 + 16 + 23	35 + 22 + 40	41 + 32 + 14	10 + 20 + 30

Subtract.

94 − 13	66 − 33	88 − 44	73 − 23	99 − 89	44 − 34
59 − 43	37 − 12	86 − 42	56 − 34	80 − 70	75 − 52

Perfect score: 30 My score: ______

Problem Solving

Solve each problem.

24 frogs in the water.

43 frogs hopping on the land.

How many frogs in all?

$$\begin{array}{r} 24 \\ +43 \\ \hline 67 \end{array}$$

---

60 boys were swimming at the beach.

40 girls came to swim.

How many more boys than girls?

The team shot 55 baskets.

The team missed 24 baskets.

How many baskets did the team make?

There are 44 rows of corn in a field.

There are 53 rows of corn in the other field.

How many rows of corn in all?

Lee pounds 14 posts in the ground.

Damien pounds 23 posts.

Dale pounds 32 posts.

How many posts did the boys pound in the ground?

Perfect score: 5 My score: ______

NAME ____________________

Chapter 5 Checkup

Add.

44	62	40	58	71	35
+24	+35	+30	+41	+25	+53

5	25	41	34	52	22
2	33	50	42	31	41
+1	+11	+ 4	+11	+14	+15

5

Subtract.

25	75	86	93	67	60
−13	−24	−53	−23	−36	−30

49	46	58	76	82	95
−38	−22	−43	−30	−41	−44

Solve each problem.

Ryan had 53¢. ____ ¢

Corbet had 32¢ + ____ ¢

Ryan and Corbet had this much. ____ ¢

Kelly had 68¢. ____ ¢

She spent 44¢. − ____ ¢

Kelly had this much left. ____ ¢

Perfect score: 26 My score: ________

Add.

23	16	13	37	53
+19	+17	+28	+18	+39
47	57	73	49	64
+23	+34	+18	+11	+18
25	24	26	35	51
+16	+37	+18	+16	+29

Subtract.

42	24	34	44	93
−18	−18	−17	−35	−74
86	75	66	51	22
−37	−38	−49	−27	−18
31	43	52	71	82
−18	−24	−36	−43	−66

Perfect score: 30 My score: ________

NAME ____________________

Lesson 1 Addition and Subtraction Review

Add.

4	8	9	7	5	6
+9	+6	+8	+6	+7	+5

9	5	7	9	8	7
+6	+8	+4	+9	+7	+9

30	20	45	52	60	83
+40	+30	+23	+23	+25	+15

Subtract.

16	15	13	12	11	17
−7	−9	−4	−7	−9	−8

18	17	16	15	14	16
−9	−9	−8	−8	−7	−9

40	60	85	73	96	54
−30	−10	−23	−41	−43	−44

Perfect score: 36 My score: ________

Addition and Subtraction Review

Add.

4 +8	9 +2	5 +9	6 +6	7 +5	9 +4
8 +8	7 +6	3 +9	7 +7	6 +9	6 +5
40 +20	50 +30	75 +20	66 +31	47 +51	34 +23

Subtract.

17 − 9	15 − 6	12 − 3	13 − 7	14 − 6	16 − 8
15 − 7	14 − 9	13 − 6	15 − 7	12 − 9	11 − 8
30 −10	50 −30	65 −30	87 −34	75 −23	66 −43

Perfect score: 36 My score: ______

NAME ______________________

Lesson 2 Addition

Add the ones.

$$\begin{array}{r} 56 \\ +29 \\ \hline \end{array} \qquad \begin{array}{r} 6 \\ +9 \\ \hline 15 \end{array} \text{ or } 10 + 5$$

Rename 15 as 10 + 5.

$$\begin{array}{r} ^{1} \\ 56 \\ +29 \\ \hline 5 \end{array}$$

Add the tens.

$$\begin{array}{r} ^{1} \\ 56 \\ +29 \\ \hline 85 \end{array}$$

Add the ones.

$$\begin{array}{r} 47 \\ +35 \\ \hline \end{array} \qquad \begin{array}{r} 7 \\ +5 \\ \hline 12 \end{array} \text{ or } 10 + 2$$

Rename 12 as 10 + 2.

$$\begin{array}{r} ^{1} \\ 47 \\ +35 \\ \hline 2 \end{array}$$

Add the tens.

$$\begin{array}{r} ^{1} \\ 47 \\ +35 \\ \hline 82 \end{array}$$

Add.

$\begin{array}{r} 45 \\ +28 \\ \hline 73 \end{array}$	$\begin{array}{r} 13 \\ +19 \\ \hline 32 \end{array}$	$\begin{array}{r} 48 \\ +35 \\ \hline \end{array}$	$\begin{array}{r} 69 \\ +18 \\ \hline \end{array}$	$\begin{array}{r} 54 \\ +39 \\ \hline \end{array}$
$\begin{array}{r} 44 \\ +17 \\ \hline \end{array}$	$\begin{array}{r} 37 \\ +18 \\ \hline \end{array}$	$\begin{array}{r} 28 \\ +36 \\ \hline \end{array}$	$\begin{array}{r} 73 \\ +18 \\ \hline \end{array}$	$\begin{array}{r} 66 \\ +29 \\ \hline \end{array}$
$\begin{array}{r} 52 \\ +39 \\ \hline \end{array}$	$\begin{array}{r} 38 \\ +47 \\ \hline \end{array}$	$\begin{array}{r} 64 \\ +18 \\ \hline \end{array}$	$\begin{array}{r} 29 \\ +45 \\ \hline \end{array}$	$\begin{array}{r} 75 \\ +17 \\ \hline \end{array}$

Perfect score: 15 My score: __________

Addition (2 digit)

Add the ones.			Rename 11 as 10 + 1.		Add the tens.
3 8	8	➡	1	➡	1
+4 3	+3		3 8		3 8
	11 or 10 + 1		+4 3		+4 3
			1		8 1

Add.

$17 + 34 = 51$	$26 + 47$	$47 + 35$	$68 + 24$	$37 + 28$
$29 + 48$	$58 + 27$	$69 + 17$	$78 + 13$	$19 + 44$
$55 + 28$	$27 + 35$	$39 + 52$	$57 + 27$	$38 + 36$
$49 + 43$	$65 + 18$	$23 + 18$	$64 + 18$	$46 + 39$
$54 + 27$	$38 + 44$	$66 + 26$	$28 + 34$	$19 + 56$

Perfect score: 25 My score: ________

NAME ______________________

Lesson 3 Addition (2 digit)

Add the ones.		Rename 12 as 10 + 2.	Add the tens.
$\begin{array}{r} 64 \\ +28 \\ \hline \end{array}$	$\begin{array}{r} 4 \\ +8 \\ \hline 12 \end{array}$ 12 or 10 + 2	$\begin{array}{r} 1 \\ 64 \\ +28 \\ \hline 2 \end{array}$	$\begin{array}{r} 1 \\ 64 \\ +28 \\ \hline 92 \end{array}$

Add.

$\begin{array}{r} 28 \\ +19 \\ \hline 47 \end{array}$	$\begin{array}{r} 34 \\ +49 \\ \hline \end{array}$	$\begin{array}{r} 25 \\ +16 \\ \hline \end{array}$	$\begin{array}{r} 46 \\ +29 \\ \hline \end{array}$	$\begin{array}{r} 54 \\ +39 \\ \hline \end{array}$
$\begin{array}{r} 16 \\ +39 \\ \hline \end{array}$	$\begin{array}{r} 64 \\ +28 \\ \hline \end{array}$	$\begin{array}{r} 58 \\ +24 \\ \hline \end{array}$	$\begin{array}{r} 39 \\ +17 \\ \hline \end{array}$	$\begin{array}{r} 34 \\ +19 \\ \hline \end{array}$
$\begin{array}{r} 57 \\ +39 \\ \hline \end{array}$	$\begin{array}{r} 14 \\ +48 \\ \hline \end{array}$	$\begin{array}{r} 37 \\ +39 \\ \hline \end{array}$	$\begin{array}{r} 61 \\ +19 \\ \hline \end{array}$	$\begin{array}{r} 29 \\ +44 \\ \hline \end{array}$
$\begin{array}{r} 17 \\ +35 \\ \hline \end{array}$	$\begin{array}{r} 39 \\ +14 \\ \hline \end{array}$	$\begin{array}{r} 44 \\ +37 \\ \hline \end{array}$	$\begin{array}{r} 25 \\ +49 \\ \hline \end{array}$	$\begin{array}{r} 18 \\ +18 \\ \hline \end{array}$
$\begin{array}{r} 26 \\ +48 \\ \hline \end{array}$	$\begin{array}{r} 39 \\ +27 \\ \hline \end{array}$	$\begin{array}{r} 14 \\ +27 \\ \hline \end{array}$	$\begin{array}{r} 65 \\ +25 \\ \hline \end{array}$	$\begin{array}{r} 59 \\ +18 \\ \hline \end{array}$

Perfect score: 25 My score: ________

Problem Solving

Solve each problem.

16 boys ride their bikes to school.

18 girls ride their bikes to school.

How many bikes are ridden to school?

$$\begin{array}{r} 16 \\ +\,18 \\ \hline 34 \end{array}$$

Dad reads 26 pages.

Mike reads 37 pages.

How many pages did Dad and Mike read?

Mary counts 46 stars.

Mike counts 39 stars.

How many stars did they count?

Mom has 29 golf balls.

Uncle Sam has 43 golf balls.

How many golf balls do they have?

Vicki ran in 26 races.

Kay ran in 14 races.

How many races did they run?

Perfect score: 5 My score: ________

NAME ____________________

Lesson 4 Addition (2 digit)

Add.

36 +55	14 +28	57 +38	44 +48	33 +29
23 +18	27 +27	68 +25	23 +19	42 +19
56 +28	49 +27	38 +49	36 +18	49 +24
18 +54	51 +39	74 +17	35 +28	52 +19
48 +26	25 +28	39 +33	29 +44	54 +27

Perfect score: 25 My score: ________

Problem Solving

Solve each problem.

Simon sees 36 birds flying.

Julie sees 28 birds flying.

How many birds do they see flying?

$$\begin{array}{r} 36 \\ +28 \\ \hline 64 \end{array}$$

Brandon ran the race in 35 seconds.

Ryan ran the race in 28 seconds.

How many seconds did they run?

Tom has 63 nickels.

Connie has 29 nickels.

How many nickels do they have?

Pam sees 48 monkeys at the zoo.

Brenda sees 35 different monkeys.

How many monkeys did they see?

There are 29 steers in one pen.

There are 47 steers in the other pen.

How many steers in all?

Perfect score: 5 My score: ________

NAME ______________________

Lesson 5 Subtraction (2 digits)

Rename 53 as 4 tens and 13 ones. → Subtract the ones. → Subtract the tens.

```
 5 3      4 13        4 13        4 13
-2 6      5̸ 3̸         5̸ 3̸         5̸ 3̸
         -2 6        -2 6        -2 6
                        7         2 7
```

Rename 45 as 3 tens and 15 ones. → Subtract the ones. → Subtract the tens.

```
 4 5      3 15        3 15        3 15
-1 8      4̸ 5̸         4̸ 5̸         4̸ 5̸
         -1 8        -1 8        -1 8
                        7         2 7
```

Subtract.

```
 5 13     6 14
 6̸ 3̸      7̸ 4̸       4 7     5 2     6 4
-2 8     -3 9      -2 8    -2 6    -3 6
  35       35

 8 4      9 3       7 1     2 6     6 7
-4 7     -5 6      -2 3    -1 8    -4 8

 4 4      5 3       8 2     9 4     5 5
-2 8     -3 7      -4 6    -6 6    -3 9

 8 6      3 4       5 4     7 3     8 6
-5 8     -1 8      -2 9    -5 9    -6 9
```


Perfect score: 20 My score: ________

Subtraction (2 digit)

Rename 73 as 6 tens and 13 ones.		Subtract the ones.	Subtract the tens.
$\begin{array}{r} 73 \\ -48 \\ \hline \end{array}$	$\begin{array}{r} {\scriptstyle 6\,13} \\ \not{7}\,\not{3} \\ -4\,8 \\ \hline \end{array}$	$\begin{array}{r} {\scriptstyle 6\,13} \\ \not{7}\,\not{3} \\ -4\,8 \\ \hline 5 \end{array}$	$\begin{array}{r} {\scriptstyle 6\,13} \\ \not{7}\,\not{3} \\ -4\,8 \\ \hline 2\,5 \end{array}$

Subtract.

$\begin{array}{r} {\scriptstyle 5\,13} \\ \not{6}\,\not{3} \\ -4\,8 \\ \hline 1\,5 \end{array}$	$\begin{array}{r} 83 \\ -45 \\ \hline \end{array}$	$\begin{array}{r} 74 \\ -29 \\ \hline \end{array}$	$\begin{array}{r} 94 \\ -48 \\ \hline \end{array}$	$\begin{array}{r} 62 \\ -25 \\ \hline \end{array}$
$\begin{array}{r} 45 \\ -27 \\ \hline \end{array}$	$\begin{array}{r} 33 \\ -24 \\ \hline \end{array}$	$\begin{array}{r} 24 \\ -18 \\ \hline \end{array}$	$\begin{array}{r} 86 \\ -37 \\ \hline \end{array}$	$\begin{array}{r} 72 \\ -48 \\ \hline \end{array}$
$\begin{array}{r} 36 \\ -17 \\ \hline \end{array}$	$\begin{array}{r} 26 \\ -18 \\ \hline \end{array}$	$\begin{array}{r} 43 \\ -19 \\ \hline \end{array}$	$\begin{array}{r} 63 \\ -48 \\ \hline \end{array}$	$\begin{array}{r} 93 \\ -18 \\ \hline \end{array}$
$\begin{array}{r} 82 \\ -26 \\ \hline \end{array}$	$\begin{array}{r} 73 \\ -28 \\ \hline \end{array}$	$\begin{array}{r} 95 \\ -69 \\ \hline \end{array}$	$\begin{array}{r} 57 \\ -38 \\ \hline \end{array}$	$\begin{array}{r} 41 \\ -25 \\ \hline \end{array}$
$\begin{array}{r} 54 \\ -18 \\ \hline \end{array}$	$\begin{array}{r} 61 \\ -34 \\ \hline \end{array}$	$\begin{array}{r} 91 \\ -37 \\ \hline \end{array}$	$\begin{array}{r} 81 \\ -44 \\ \hline \end{array}$	$\begin{array}{r} 32 \\ -15 \\ \hline \end{array}$

Perfect score: 25 My score: ________

Lesson 6 Subtraction (2 digit)

NAME ____________________

Rename 61 as 5 tens and 11 ones.		Subtract the ones.	Subtract the tens.
$\begin{array}{r} 61 \\ -43 \\ \hline \end{array}$	$\begin{array}{r} \scriptstyle 5\ 11 \\ \not6\,\not1 \\ -4\ 3 \\ \hline \end{array}$	$\begin{array}{r} \scriptstyle 5\ 11 \\ \not6\,\not1 \\ -4\ 3 \\ \hline 8 \end{array}$	$\begin{array}{r} \scriptstyle 5\ 11 \\ \not6\,\not1 \\ -4\ 3 \\ \hline 1\ 8 \end{array}$

Subtract.

$\begin{array}{r} \scriptstyle 3\ 17 \\ \not4\,\not7 \\ -2\ 8 \\ \hline 1\ 9 \end{array}$	$\begin{array}{r} 73 \\ -48 \\ \hline \end{array}$	$\begin{array}{r} 84 \\ -66 \\ \hline \end{array}$	$\begin{array}{r} 95 \\ -18 \\ \hline \end{array}$	$\begin{array}{r} 64 \\ -29 \\ \hline \end{array}$
$\begin{array}{r} 56 \\ -38 \\ \hline \end{array}$	$\begin{array}{r} 31 \\ -15 \\ \hline \end{array}$	$\begin{array}{r} 25 \\ -17 \\ \hline \end{array}$	$\begin{array}{r} 33 \\ -19 \\ \hline \end{array}$	$\begin{array}{r} 46 \\ -29 \\ \hline \end{array}$
$\begin{array}{r} 93 \\ -64 \\ \hline \end{array}$	$\begin{array}{r} 82 \\ -55 \\ \hline \end{array}$	$\begin{array}{r} 72 \\ -14 \\ \hline \end{array}$	$\begin{array}{r} 45 \\ -28 \\ \hline \end{array}$	$\begin{array}{r} 61 \\ -23 \\ \hline \end{array}$
$\begin{array}{r} 51 \\ -44 \\ \hline \end{array}$	$\begin{array}{r} 62 \\ -48 \\ \hline \end{array}$	$\begin{array}{r} 37 \\ -19 \\ \hline \end{array}$	$\begin{array}{r} 50 \\ -32 \\ \hline \end{array}$	$\begin{array}{r} 83 \\ -47 \\ \hline \end{array}$
$\begin{array}{r} 92 \\ -73 \\ \hline \end{array}$	$\begin{array}{r} 82 \\ -75 \\ \hline \end{array}$	$\begin{array}{r} 76 \\ -38 \\ \hline \end{array}$	$\begin{array}{r} 47 \\ -29 \\ \hline \end{array}$	$\begin{array}{r} 74 \\ -39 \\ \hline \end{array}$

Perfect score: 25 My score: __________

Problem Solving

Solve each problem.

Dad cooks 23 potatoes.

He uses 19 potatoes in the potato salad.

How many potatoes are left?

$$\begin{array}{r} {\scriptstyle 1\ 13} \\ 23 \\ -19 \\ \hline 4 \end{array}$$

Susan draws 32 butterflies.

She colored 15 of them brown.

How many butterflies does she have left to color?

A book has 66 pages.

Pedro reads 39 pages.

How many pages are left to read?

Jerry picks up 34 sea shells.

He puts 15 of them in a box.

How many does he have left?

Beth buys 72 sheets of paper.

She uses 44 sheets for her school work.

How many sheets of paper are left?

Perfect score: 5 My score: ______

NAME ______________________

Lesson 7 Subtraction

Subtract.

$\begin{array}{r}85\\-16\\\hline\end{array}$	$\begin{array}{r}93\\-48\\\hline\end{array}$	$\begin{array}{r}72\\-35\\\hline\end{array}$	$\begin{array}{r}63\\-27\\\hline\end{array}$	$\begin{array}{r}43\\-38\\\hline\end{array}$
$\begin{array}{r}56\\-29\\\hline\end{array}$	$\begin{array}{r}75\\-49\\\hline\end{array}$	$\begin{array}{r}84\\-38\\\hline\end{array}$	$\begin{array}{r}91\\-65\\\hline\end{array}$	$\begin{array}{r}37\\-18\\\hline\end{array}$
$\begin{array}{r}21\\-14\\\hline\end{array}$	$\begin{array}{r}35\\-18\\\hline\end{array}$	$\begin{array}{r}42\\-29\\\hline\end{array}$	$\begin{array}{r}72\\-47\\\hline\end{array}$	$\begin{array}{r}81\\-54\\\hline\end{array}$
$\begin{array}{r}64\\-38\\\hline\end{array}$	$\begin{array}{r}53\\-28\\\hline\end{array}$	$\begin{array}{r}94\\-57\\\hline\end{array}$	$\begin{array}{r}48\\-39\\\hline\end{array}$	$\begin{array}{r}23\\-18\\\hline\end{array}$
$\begin{array}{r}74\\-58\\\hline\end{array}$	$\begin{array}{r}83\\-36\\\hline\end{array}$	$\begin{array}{r}62\\-26\\\hline\end{array}$	$\begin{array}{r}54\\-28\\\hline\end{array}$	$\begin{array}{r}32\\-17\\\hline\end{array}$

Perfect score: 25 My score: __________

Problem Solving

Solve each problem.

Scott has 80 pennies.

Tracy has 45 pennies.

How many pennies in all?

$$\begin{array}{r} 40 \\ +45 \\ \hline 85 \end{array}$$

Mom puts 36 nails in a box.

Edna takes 18 nails out of the box.

How many nails are left in the box?

Liz buys 57 apples and oranges.

29 are oranges.

How many are apples?

Tony can jump a rope 84 times.

Curt can jump a rope 69 times.

How many more times can Tony jump than Curt?

The team scored 74 points.

Michelle scored 37 of the points.

How many points did the rest of the team score?

Perfect score: 5 My score: ______

NAME ________________________

Lesson 8 Addition and Subtraction (2 digit)

Add.

64 +29	37 +46	24 +19	71 +19	49 +18
27 +44	33 +18	28 +25	59 +16	34 +48
43 +29	26 +45	72 +19	69 +15	18 +39

Subtract.

76 −48	67 −59	88 −69	93 −48	45 −27
84 −16	95 −27	36 −18	63 −28	72 −49
91 −32	72 −45	62 −18	54 −36	33 −19

Perfect score: 30 My score: ________

Solve each problem.

Mr. Smith milks 64  .

Mr. Jones milks 29  .

How many more  does Mr. Smith milk than Mr. Jones?

$$\begin{array}{r} {\scriptstyle 5\ 14} \\ \not{6}\not{4} \\ -\ 29 \\ \hline 35 \end{array}$$

There are 13 girls playing  .

18 more girls join in to play.

How many girls are playing  ?

Sally served the  34 times.

Jeff served the  19 times.

How many more times did Sally serve?

---

62 red  grew in the garden.

29 yellow  grew there too.

How many  grew in the garden?

Jon has 62 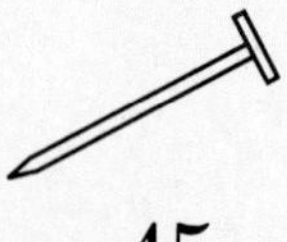 .

He hammers 45 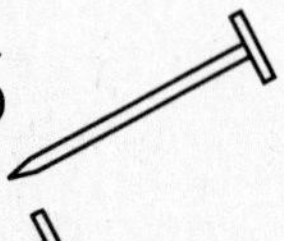 in the board.

How many 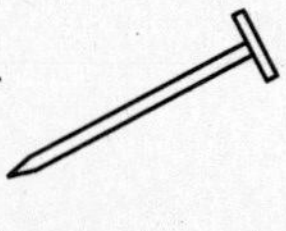 does Jon have left?

Perfect score: 5 My score: ________

NAME ____________________

Chapter 6 Checkup

Add.

24 + 18	56 + 27	49 + 26	62 + 19	39 + 18
28 + 34	73 + 19	64 + 18	59 + 33	13 + 18

Subtract.

53 − 27	76 − 47	97 − 78	62 − 38	44 − 26
84 − 39	38 − 29	25 − 18	82 − 48	96 − 79

Solve each problem.

There are 26 pieces of chalk on the chalkboard.

18 pieces fall on the floor. −

How many pieces are still on the chalkboard?

Jason did 26 pages of homework.

Beth did 36 pages of homework. +

How many pages of homework did they do in all?

Perfect score: 22 My score: ________

NAME ____________

PRE-TEST

Write the numerals.

5 hundreds 3 tens 2 ones ______	8 hundreds 4 tens 1 one ______
4 hundreds 8 tens 6 ones ______	3 hundreds 7 tens 8 ones ______

7

Add.

300 + 100	600 + 300	200 + 300	500 + 200
569 + 120	432 + 246	215 + 442	626 + 13

Subtract.

400 − 300	800 − 100	600 − 400	300 − 200
846 − 321	768 − 616	346 − 32	585 − 261

Perfect score: 20 My score: ______

NAME ______________________

Lesson 1 Numbers 100 Through 199

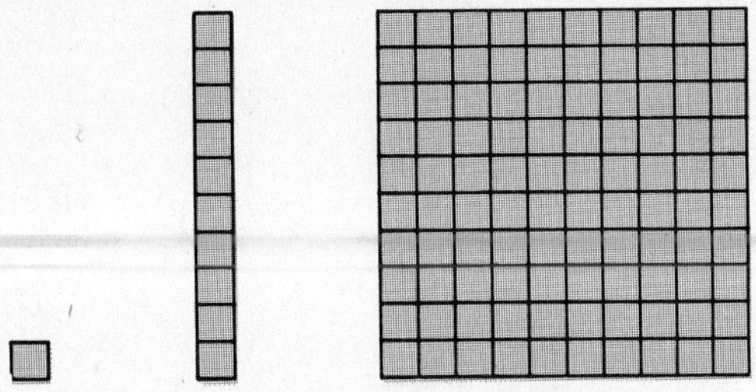

one | ten | ten tens or one hundred

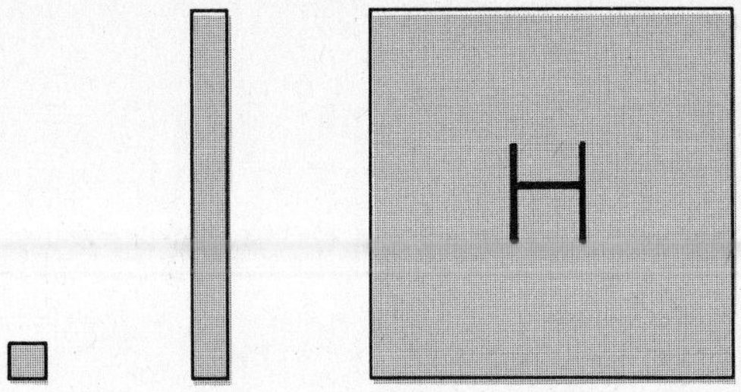

1 | 10 | 100

Write the numerals.

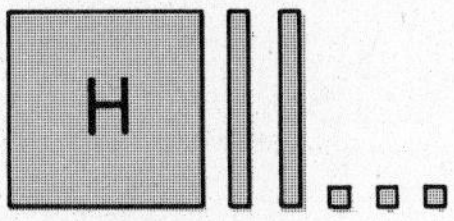

1 hundred 2 tens 3 ones

123

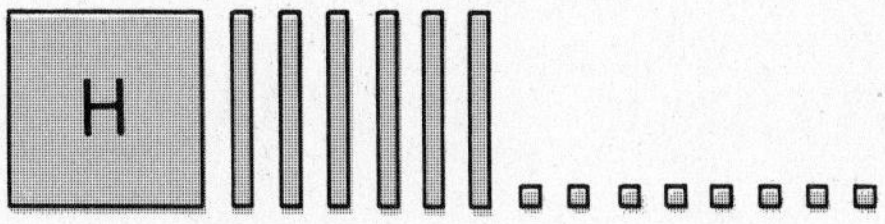

__ hundred __ tens __ ones

______

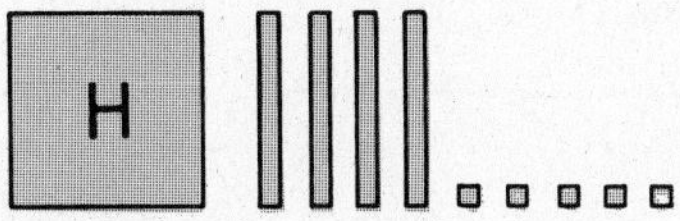

__ hundred __ tens __ ones

______

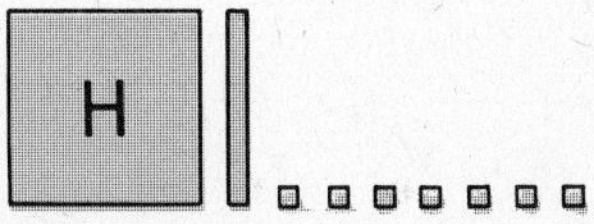

__ hundred __ ten __ ones

______

1 hundred 5 tens 0 ones

150

1 hundred 7 tens 2 ones

______

1 hundred 0 tens 4 ones

______

1 hundred 9 tens 9 ones

______

Perfect score: 20 My score: ______

NAME ____________________

Lesson 2 Numbers 200 Through 499

Write the numerals.

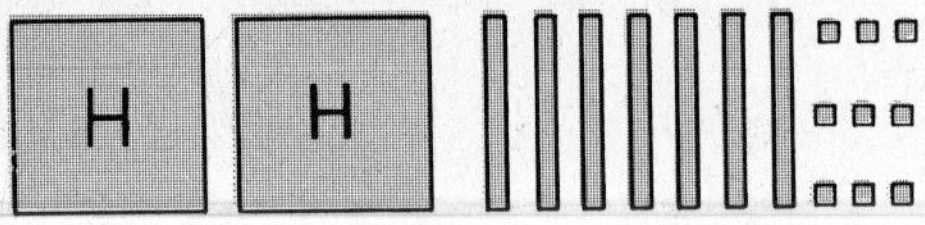

2 hundreds 7 tens 9 ones

279

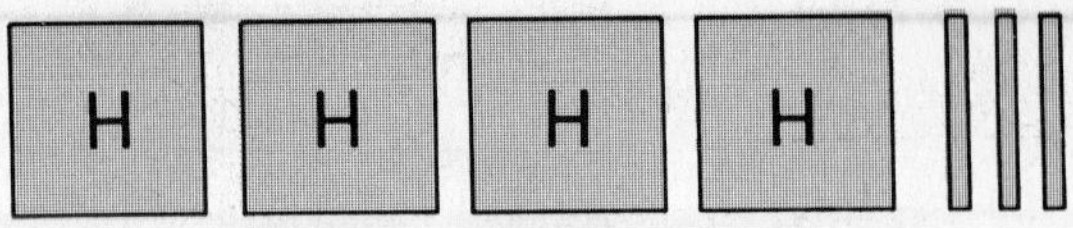

4 hundreds 3 tens 0 ones

______

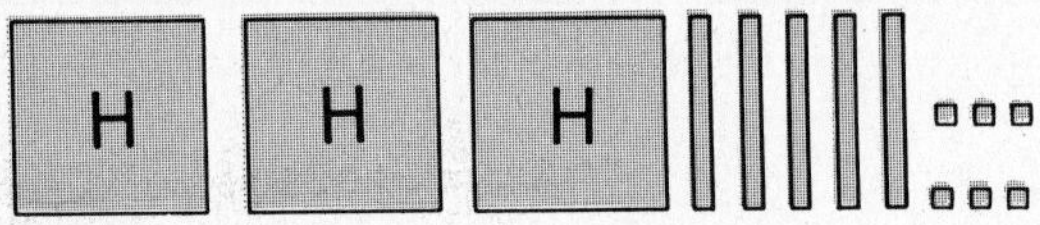

___ hundreds ___ tens ___ ones

______

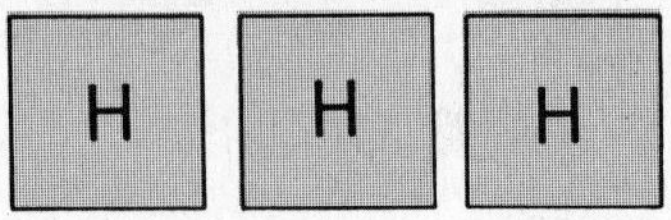

___ hundreds ___ tens ___ ones

______

2 hundreds 3 tens 6 ones

______

3 hundreds 4 tens 0 ones

______

4 hundreds 9 tens 9 ones

______

2 hundreds 8 tens 9 ones

______

4 hundreds 0 tens 4 ones

______

3 hundreds 2 tens 1 one

______

Name the numbers in order.

265, 266, ______, ______, ______, ______, ______

398, 399, ______, ______, ______, ______, ______

SPECTRUM MATHEMATICS,
Brown Book

Perfect score: 34 My score: ______

NAME ________________________

Lesson 3 Numbers 500 Through 799

Write the numerals.

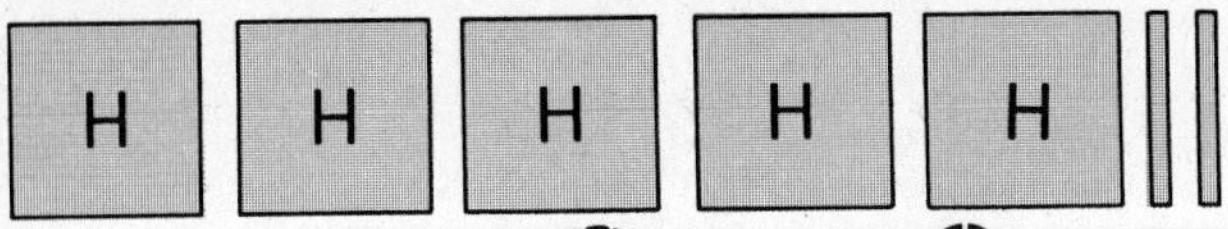	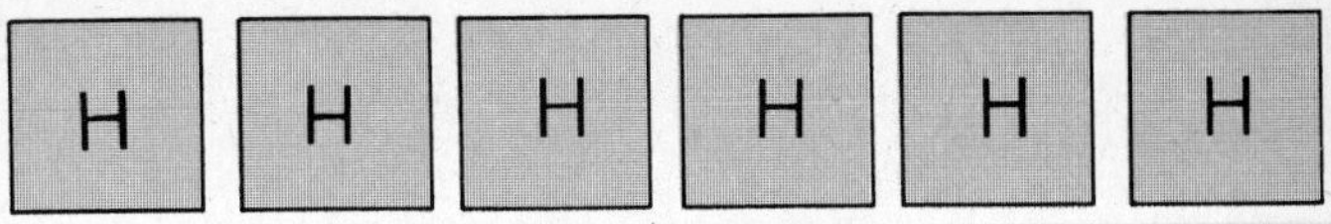
5 hundreds 2 tens 0 ones ________	___ hundreds ___ tens ___ ones ________
6 hundreds 2 tens 1 one ________	7 hundreds 1 ten 4 ones ________
5 hundreds 5 tens 3 ones ________	6 hundreds 9 tens 7 ones ________
6 hundreds 7 tens 8 ones ________	7 hundreds 3 tens 2 ones ________
7 hundreds 6 tens 5 ones ________	5 hundreds 8 tens 3 ones ________
6 hundreds 1 ten 0 ones ________	7 hundreds 7 tens 6 ones ________
7 hundreds 9 tens 9 ones ________	5 hundreds 8 tens 8 ones ________

Perfect score: 20 My score: ________

NAME ______________________

Lesson 4 Numbers 800 Through 999

Write the numerals.

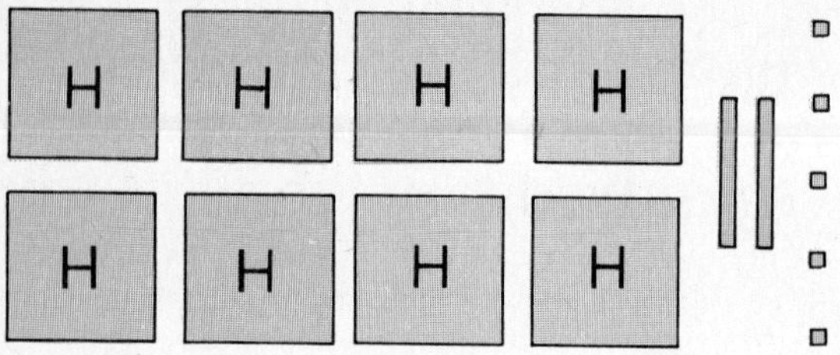

8 hundreds 2 tens 5 ones

____

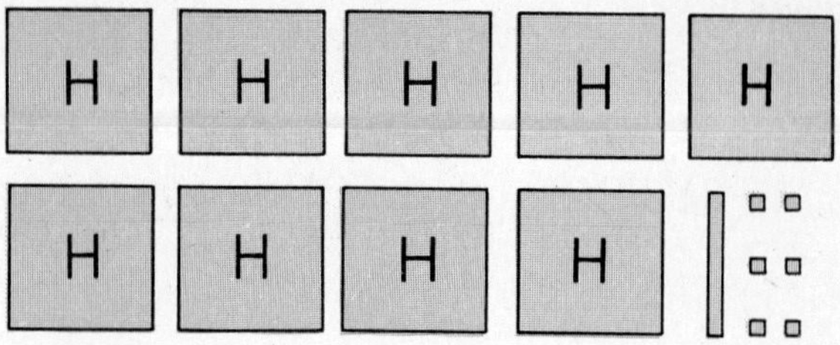

___ hundreds ___ ten ___ ones

____

9 hundreds 2 tens 8 ones

____

8 hundreds 4 tens 2 ones

____

8 hundreds 9 tens 2 ones

____

9 hundreds 0 tens 3 ones

____

9 hundreds 7 tens 5 ones

____

8 hundreds 4 tens 0 ones

____

Count by hundreds to complete the row.

100, 200, _____, _____, _____, _____, _____, _____, 900

Count by tens to complete the row.

850, 860, _____, _____, _____, _____, _____, _____, _____

Perfect score: 28 My score: ________

NAME ____________________

Lesson 5 Numbers 100 Through 999

Write the numerals.

8 hundreds 6 tens 4 ones ________	5 hundreds 3 tens 8 ones ________
3 hundreds 1 ten 5 ones ________	9 hundreds 8 tens 3 ones ________
1 hundred 0 tens 1 one ________	4 hundreds 2 tens 7 ones ________

Start at 780.
Connect the dots in order.

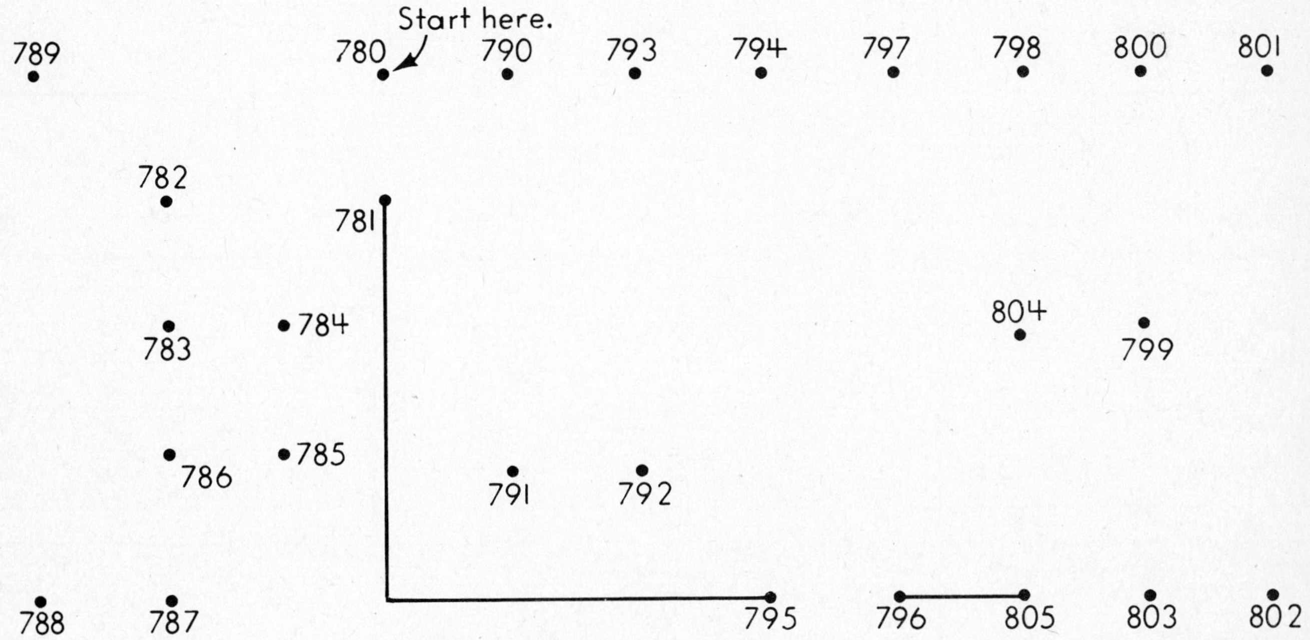

Perfect score: 7 My score: ________

Numbers 100 Through 999

Complete.

After	*Between*	*Before*
419, 420	818, 819, 820	770, 771
301, ____	324, ____, 326	____, 346
143, ____	606, ____, 608	____, 160
854, ____	255, ____, 257	____, 200
209, ____	172, ____, 174	____, 423
688, ____	760, ____, 762	____, 950
579, ____	939, ____, 941	____, 667
993, ____	499, ____, 501	____, 181
629, ____	847, ____, 849	____, 800
799, ____	583, ____, 585	____, 595

Perfect score: 30 My score: ____

Lesson 6 Adding Hundreds

NAME ______________________

5 hundreds +3 hundreds 8 hundreds	500 +300 800	4 hundreds +5 hundreds 9 hundreds	400 +500 900

Add.

3 hundreds +1 hundred 4 hundreds	300 +100 400	6 hundreds +2 hundreds hundreds	600 +200
200 +200	100 +700	600 +300	400 +500
300 +400	800 +100	400 +400	700 +200
500 +100	100 +600	500 +200	300 +200
300 +300	400 +200	300 +500	200 +100

Perfect score: 20 My score: ________

Problem Solving

Solve each problem.

Ria packed 300 boxes.

Melvin packed 200 boxes.

How many boxes did Ria and Melvin pack?

$$\begin{array}{r} 300 \\ +\,200 \\ \hline 500 \end{array}$$

Santo typed 500 letters.

Hale typed 400 letters.

How many letters did they type?

Paula used 100 paper clips.

Milton used 600 paper clips.

How many paper clips did they use?

The grocery store sold 400 red apples.

The grocery store also sold 100 yellow apples.

How many apples did the grocery store sell in all?

Miles worked 200 days.

Julia worked 500 days.

How many days did they work?

Perfect score: 5 My score: ______

Lesson 7 Addition (3 digit)

NAME ______________________

$$\begin{array}{r} 245 \\ +253 \\ \hline 8 \end{array} \rightarrow \begin{array}{r} 245 \\ +253 \\ \hline 98 \end{array} \rightarrow \begin{array}{r} 245 \\ +253 \\ \hline 498 \end{array}$$

Add.

$$\begin{array}{r} 745 \\ +\ \ 23 \\ \hline 768 \end{array}$$

Add the ones.
Add the tens.
Add the hundreds.

$$\begin{array}{r} 623 \\ +156 \\ \hline \end{array}$$

Add the ones.
Add the tens.
Add the hundreds.

$$\begin{array}{r} 415 \\ +342 \\ \hline \end{array} \quad \begin{array}{r} 566 \\ +\ \ 33 \\ \hline \end{array} \quad \begin{array}{r} 373 \\ +221 \\ \hline \end{array} \quad \begin{array}{r} 160 \\ +334 \\ \hline \end{array}$$

$$\begin{array}{r} 835 \\ +\ \ 42 \\ \hline \end{array} \quad \begin{array}{r} 642 \\ +251 \\ \hline \end{array} \quad \begin{array}{r} 287 \\ +412 \\ \hline \end{array} \quad \begin{array}{r} 723 \\ +\ \ 45 \\ \hline \end{array}$$

$$\begin{array}{r} 133 \\ +522 \\ \hline \end{array} \quad \begin{array}{r} 454 \\ +324 \\ \hline \end{array} \quad \begin{array}{r} 314 \\ +602 \\ \hline \end{array} \quad \begin{array}{r} 654 \\ +235 \\ \hline \end{array}$$

Perfect score: 14 My score: ________

Problem Solving

Solve each problem.

Gene collected 342 rocks.

Lester collected 201 rocks.

How many rocks did they collect?

$$\begin{array}{r} 342 \\ +201 \\ \hline 543 \end{array}$$

Tina jumped the rope 403 times.

Henry jumped the rope 426 times.

How many times did they jump?

There are 210 people wearing blue hats.

There are 432 people wearing red hats.

How many hats in all?

Asta used 135 paper plates.

Clyde used 143 paper plates.

How many paper plates did they use in all?

Aunt Mary had 536 dollars.

Uncle Lewis had 423 dollars.

How many dollars did they have in all?

Perfect score: 5 My score: ______

NAME ______________________

Lesson 8 Addition (3 digit)

Add.

340 + 225 = 565	754 + 32 = 786	826 + 3	632 + 322
198 + 200	456 + 31	541 + 333	273 + 415
900 + 34	847 + 131	721 + 176	402 + 383
156 + 423	644 + 251	215 + 542	372 + 417
518 + 351	783 + 5	684 + 14	710 + 260

Perfect score: 20 My score: ________

Problem Solving

Solve each problem.

There are 236 boys in school.
There are 250 girls in school.
How many boys and girls are in school?

$$\begin{array}{r} 236 \\ +250 \\ \hline \end{array}$$

Mary saw 131 cars.
Marvin saw 268 trucks.
How many cars and trucks did they see in all?

Jack has 427 pennies.
Jill has 370 pennies.
How many pennies do they have in all?

There are 582 red apples.
There are 206 yellow apples.
How many apples are there in all?

Ann found 122 shells.
Pedro found 76 shells.
How many shells did they find?

Perfect score: 5 My score: ________

NAME ______________________

Lesson 9 Subtracting Hundreds

8 hundreds − 3 hundreds 5 hundreds	800 − 300 500	6 hundreds − 2 hundreds 4 hundreds	600 − 200 400

Subtract.

9 hundreds − 7 hundreds 2 hundreds	900 − 700 200	3 hundreds − 1 hundred hundreds	300 − 100

700 − 300	500 − 400	900 − 400	800 − 500
600 − 500	300 − 200	500 − 100	400 − 200
900 − 100	800 − 400	600 − 200	500 − 300
400 − 100	700 − 600	800 − 200	900 − 600

Perfect score: 20 My score: ________

Problem Solving

Solve each problem.

There were 400 apples in a box.

Jesse took 100 apples from the box.

How many apples are still in the box?

$$\begin{array}{r} 400 \\ -\,100 \\ \hline 300 \end{array}$$

Tommy bought 300 golf balls.

He gave Irene 200 golf balls.

How many golf balls does he have left?

The black horse ran 900 feet.

The brown horse ran 700 feet.

How many more feet did the black horse run?

The paint store has 800 gallons of paint.

It sells 300 gallons of paint.

How many gallons of paint are left?

There are 700 children.

There are 200 boys.

How many girls are there?

Perfect score: 5 My score: ______

NAME ______________________

Lesson 10 Subtraction (3 digit)

Subtract the ones.	Subtract the tens.	Subtract the hundreds.
746 − 424 = 2	746 − 424 = 22	746 − 424 = 322

Subtract.

879 − 46 = 833

- Subtract the ones.
- Subtract the tens.
- Subtract the hundreds.

586 − 142 = ____

- Subtract the ones.
- Subtract the tens.
- Subtract the hundreds.

635 − 423	478 − 241	338 − 27	957 − 734
297 − 145	846 − 325	769 − 514	653 − 142
569 − 333	365 − 213	818 − 618	936 − 424

Perfect score: 14 My score: ________

Solve each problem.

The grocery store buys 568 cans of beans.

It sells 345 cans of beans.

How many cans of beans are left?

$$\begin{array}{r} 568 \\ -\ 345 \\ \hline 223 \end{array}$$

The cooler holds 732 gallons of milk.

It has 412 gallons of milk in it.

How many more gallons of milk will it take to fill the cooler?

Ann does 635 push-ups.

Carl does 421 push-ups.

How many more push-ups does Ann do?

Kurt has 386 pennies.

Neal has 32 pennies.

How many more pennies does Kurt have?

It takes 874 nails to build a tree house.

Jillian has 532 nails.

How many more nails does she need?

Perfect score: 5 My score: ______

NAME ______________________

Lesson 11 Subtraction (3 digit)

Subtract.

856 − 352 = 504	432 − 21 = 411	598 − 416	769 − 345
319 − 6	954 − 731	275 − 3	643 − 313
775 − 261	834 − 12	942 − 111	478 − 324
562 − 431	444 − 212	385 − 152	754 − 3
868 − 234	943 − 843	689 − 417	577 − 37

Perfect score: 20 My score: ________

Problem Solving

Solve each problem.

There were 787 bales of hay.

Glenda fed the cows 535 bales.

How many bales of hay are left?

$$\begin{array}{r} 787 \\ -\,535 \\ \hline 252 \end{array}$$

There are 673 bolts in a box.

Maria took 341 bolts out of the box.

How many bolts are left in the box?

The secretary typed 459 letters.

138 of the letters were mailed.

How many letters are left?

Mr. Jones had 569 dollars

He spent 203 dollars.

How many dollars does he have left?

There are 342 riding horses in the rodeo.

There are 132 bucking horses in the rodeo.

How many more riding horses are there?

Perfect score: 5 My score: ________

NAME ______________________

Chapter 7 Checkup

Write the numerals.

1 hundred 0 tens 5 ones ______	9 hundreds 6 tens 4 ones ______
6 hundreds 1 ten 8 ones ______	3 hundreds 2 tens 7 ones ______
3 hundreds 7 tens 1 one ______	7 hundreds 1 ten 9 ones ______

7

Name the numbers in order.

497, 498, ______, ______, ______

Count by tens. Complete the row.

460, ______, ______, ______, 500

Add.

300	400	497	203
+500	+400	+100	+ 46

Continued on the next page.

Add.

$$\begin{array}{r} 124 \\ +323 \\ \hline \end{array} \qquad \begin{array}{r} 520 \\ +407 \\ \hline \end{array} \qquad \begin{array}{r} 739 \\ +150 \\ \hline \end{array} \qquad \begin{array}{r} 861 \\ +\ 6 \\ \hline \end{array}$$

Subtract.

$$\begin{array}{r} 900 \\ -600 \\ \hline \end{array} \qquad \begin{array}{r} 800 \\ -200 \\ \hline \end{array} \qquad \begin{array}{r} 974 \\ -564 \\ \hline \end{array} \qquad \begin{array}{r} 508 \\ -\ 7 \\ \hline \end{array}$$

$$\begin{array}{r} 728 \\ -326 \\ \hline \end{array} \qquad \begin{array}{r} 657 \\ -\ 45 \\ \hline \end{array} \qquad \begin{array}{r} 894 \\ -464 \\ \hline \end{array} \qquad \begin{array}{r} 596 \\ -352 \\ \hline \end{array}$$

Solve each problem.

There are 275 nails in a box.

123 nails are taken out of the box.

How many nails are still in the box?

Gerald peeled 212 apples.

Anna peeled 84 apples.

How many apples did they peel in all?

Perfect score: 30 My score: ________

NAME ______________________

Complete.

4 tens 6 ones = ______

8 tens 0 ones = ______

Name the next three numbers.

26, 27, 28, ______, ______, ______

91, 92, 93, ______, ______, ______

Count by 10.

10, 20, 30, ______, ______, ______, ______

Add.

7 + 2	5 + 0	3 + 4	8 + 2	0 + 3
8 + 4	9 + 9	4 + 7	2 + 9	9 + 7
5 + 8	8 + 9	7 + 8	6 + 6	7 + 7

Continued on the next page.

Subtract.

9 −6	4 −2	8 −5	6 −1	7 −5
10 − 2	15 − 7	13 − 5	11 − 6	17 − 8
12 − 7	18 − 9	13 − 9	15 − 6	16 − 8

How long is each object?

Use a centimeter ruler.

____ centimeters

Use an inch ruler.

____ inches

Ring the fraction that tells how much is blue.

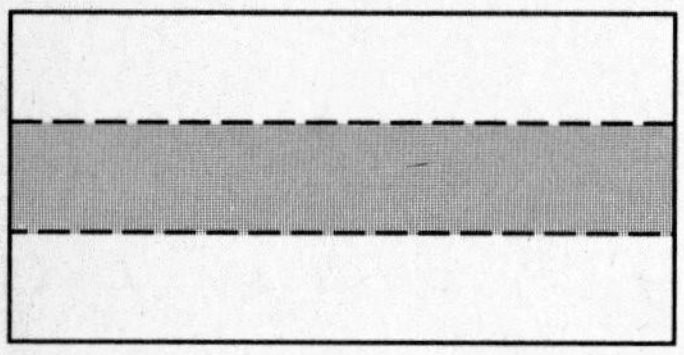

$\frac{1}{2}$ $\frac{1}{3}$ $\frac{1}{4}$

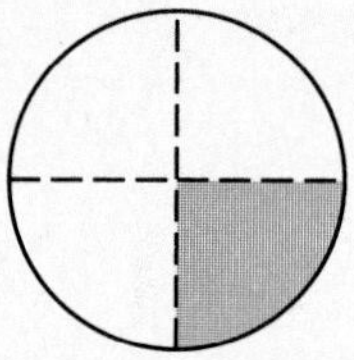

$\frac{1}{2}$ $\frac{1}{3}$ $\frac{1}{4}$

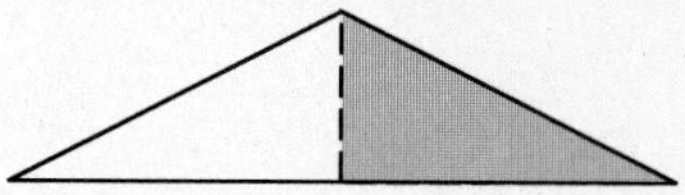

$\frac{1}{2}$ $\frac{1}{3}$ $\frac{1}{4}$

Write the time for each clock.

____:____

____:____

____:____

Perfect score: 50 My score: ____

NAME ____________________

FINAL CHECKUP

Add.

8	3	9	8	6	8
+2	+4	+6	+8	+7	+9

			3	10	12
30	41	93	2	20	24
+50	+28	+ 4	+3	+30	+51

38	25	47	200	774	291
+46	+28	+44	+500	+123	+408

Subtract.

9	7	10	12	17	15
−6	−3	− 5	− 3	− 9	− 8

60	39	82	56	96	47
−10	−21	−72	−40	−15	−31

87	50	72	175	384	875
−38	−22	−58	− 62	−270	−641

Continued on the next page.

Complete.

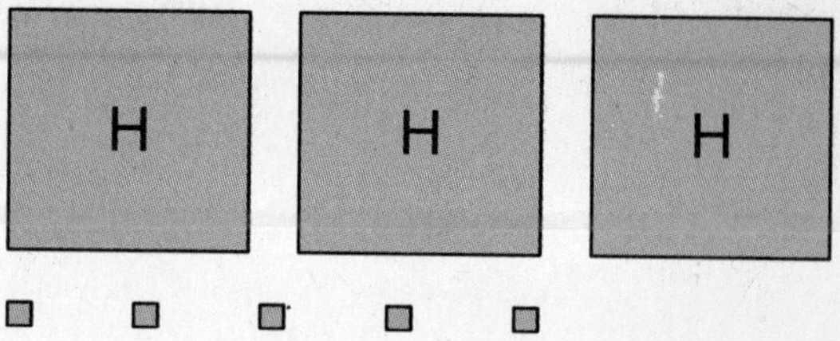

5 tens 2 ones = _____ 3 hundreds 0 tens 5 ones = _____

8 tens 9 ones = _____ 7 hundreds 3 tens 6 ones = _____

6 tens 0 ones = _____ 9 hundreds 5 tens 8 ones = _____

Name the next three numbers.

47, 48, 49, _____, _____, _____

293, 294, 295, _____, _____, _____

Count by 10.

40, 50, 60, _____, _____, _____

500, 510, 520, _____, _____, _____

Continued on the next page.

NAME ______________________

FINAL CHECKUP (Continued)

How long is each object?

Use a centimeter ruler.

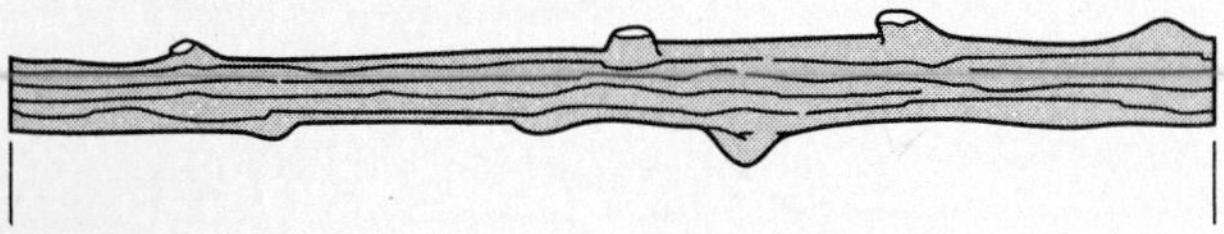

____ centimeters

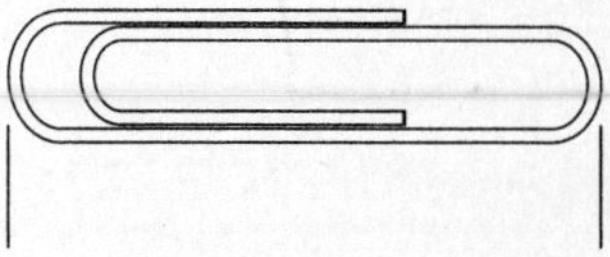

____ centimeters

Use an inch ruler.

____ inch

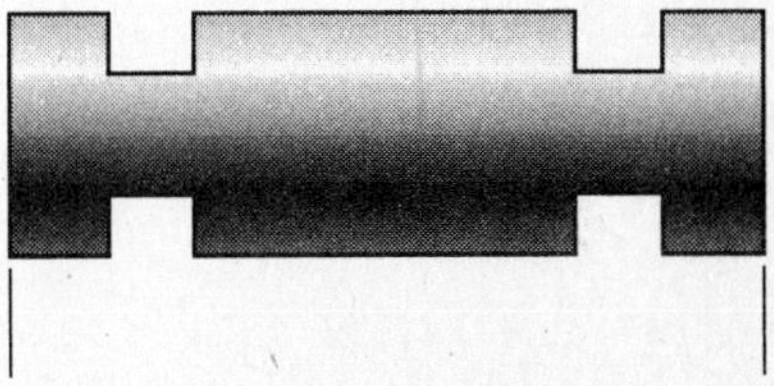

____ inches

Ring the fraction that tells how much is blue.

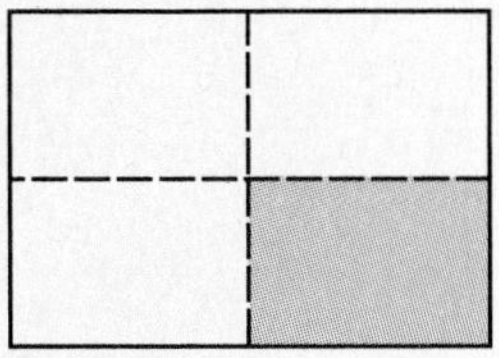

$\frac{1}{2}$ $\frac{1}{3}$ $\frac{1}{4}$

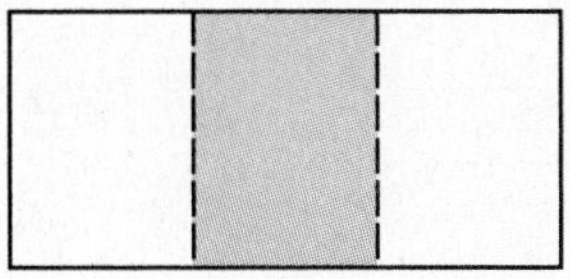

$\frac{1}{2}$ $\frac{1}{3}$ $\frac{1}{4}$

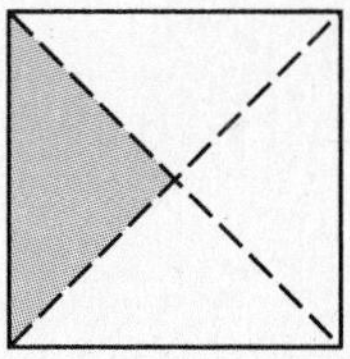

$\frac{1}{2}$ $\frac{1}{3}$ $\frac{1}{4}$

Write the time for each clock.

____:____

____:____

____:____

Continued on the next page.

Rinata has	Tao has	Cindy has	Mike has

25¢	30¢	22¢	34¢

Solve each problem.

Rinata has 25¢	Mike has 34¢
Cindy has − 22¢	Tao has + 30¢
Rinata has this much more. 3¢	Together they have this much. 64¢

Mike has ¢	Rinata has ¢
Tao has − ¢	Mike has + ¢
Mike has this much more. ¢	Together they have this much. ¢

Mike has ¢	Cindy has ¢
Rinata has − ¢	Tao has + ¢
Mike has this much more. ¢	Together they have this much. ¢

Perfect score: 70 My score: ______

Answers for
SPECTRUM MATHEMATICS (Brown Book, Third Edition)
(Answers for Pre-Tests and Checkups are given on page 123.)

Page 1

3 1
5 0
2 6
8
10
9
7
4
0 1 2 3 4 5
6 7 8 9 10

Page 2

2 1 3 3 2 1

4 4 | 4 | 4 4
3 1 | 2 | 4 0

5 5 | 5 5 | 5 5
3 2 | 4 1 | 5 0

Page 3

6 6 5 1

6 3 | 6 6 | 4 2

7 7 | 7 7 | 7 7
4 3 | 5 2 | 6 1

6 7 6 | 0 3 4

Page 4

8 8 5 3

8 | 8 8 | 8 8
4 | 6 2 | 7 1

8 7 6 8 8 8
7 1 3 3 8 6

Page 5

9 9 5 4

9 9 | 9 9 | 9 9
6 3 | 7 2 | 8 1

9 9 7 9 9 8
4 4 1 6 0 9

Page 6

10 | 10 10 | 10 10
5 | 6 4 | 7 3

10 10 | 10 10
8 2 | 9 1

10 10 10 | 2 7 10

Page 7

9 7 3 8 10 8
6 5 9 10 10 4
9 7 7 10 9 8
4 6 2 1 1 5
6 8 5 2 1 0
6 3 1 7 3 3

Page 8

$4 + 3 = 7$ $6 - 3 = 3$ $4 + 4 = 8$ $5 - 2 = 3$ $6 + 3 = 9$

Page 11

1 ten 1 one = 11
1 ten 2 ones = 12
1 ten 3 ones = 13
1 ten 4 ones = 14
1 ten 5 ones = 15
1 ten 6 ones = 16
1 ten 7 ones = 17
1 ten 8 ones = 18

Page 12

2	20		2	5	25
1	9	19	2	8	28
3	30		3	2	32
2	6	26	3	8	38

Page 13

4	40		4	2	42
5	6	56	6	5	65
7	70		7	9	79
8	7	87	9	3	93

Page 14

4	5	45	4	3	43
5	50		5	8	58
6	6	66	7	2	72
8	80		9	9	99

Page 15

46 21
12 57
37 78 19 41
24 11 88 34
90 84 67 66
60 35 72 89
53 49 95 20
96 50

Page 16

0	1	2	3	4	5	6	7	8	9
10	11	12	13	14	15	16	17	18	19
20	21	22	23	24	25	26	27	28	29
30	31	32	33	34	35	36	37	38	39
40	41	42	43	44	45	46	47	48	49
50	51	52	53	54	55	56	57	58	59

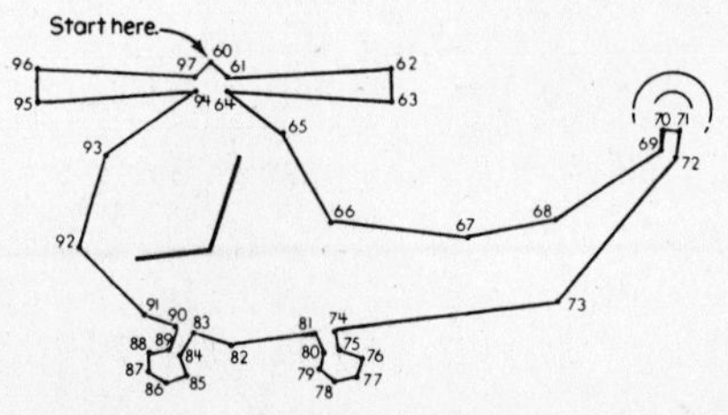

Page 17

9 10 11 12
25 26 27 28
40 41 42 43
18 19 20 21
54 55 56 57
47 48 49 50
79 80 81 82
85 86 87 88
71 72 73 74
89 90 91 92
58 59 60 61
96 97 98 99

Page 18

10 20 30 40 50
60 70 80 90
5 10 15 20 25
30 35 40 45 50
55 60 65 70 75

Page 21

11 11 | 11 11
11 11 | 11 11
12 12 | 12 12
12 12 | 12

11 12 12 11 11 11
12 12 12 11 11 12

Page 22

$6 + 5 = 11$ $8 + 4 = 12$ $6 + 6 = 12$ $8 + 3 = 11$ $9 + 3 = 12$

Page 23

2 9 | 3 8
5 6 | 4 7
4 8 | 5 7
3 9 | 6

8 5 9 3 5 3
4 8 7 6 9 4

Page 24

$11 - 4 = 7$ $12 - 4 = 8$ $11 - 5 = 6$ $12 - 7 = 5$ $11 - 9 = 2$

Page 25

13 13 | 13 13
13 13 | 14 14
14 14 | 14

14 13 13 14 13 14
13 14 14 12 13 13

Answers

Page 26

8	5
6	9
7	9

5	8	9	5	3	9
8	4	8	4	7	6
5	4	6	9	7	5

Page 27

15	15	15	15
16	16	17	17
16		18	

15	15	18	16	17	15
17	16	16	15	14	14
12	13	13	14	13	12

Page 28

9	9	7	6	9
+9	+7	+8	+8	+8
18	16	15	14	17

Page 29

8	7
9	9

9	8	8	8	8	4
9	6	9	7	9	8
7	7	7	5	8	9
9	6	9	4	5	8

Page 30

12	10	16	14	18
−3	−3	−8	−9	−9
9	7	8	5	9

Page 31

16	14	15	13	18	14
15	14	14	16	17	13
16	14	15	13	17	15
7	2	8	6	6	9
4	5	6	4	9	5
7	8	6	7	9	5

Page 32

18	14	10	13	7
−9	−6	+7	−4	+9
9	8	17	9	16

Page 33

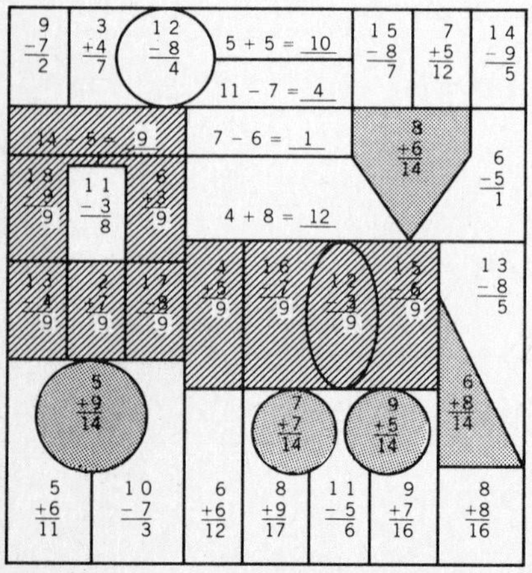

Page 34

17	9	18	8	16
−8	+7	−9	+7	−8
9	16	9	15	8

Page 37

1 2 $\frac{1}{2}$	1 2 $\frac{1}{2}$
1 2 $\frac{1}{2}$	1 2 $\frac{1}{2}$
$\frac{1}{2}$	$\frac{1}{2}$

Page 38

1 3 $\frac{1}{3}$	1 3 $\frac{1}{3}$
1 3 $\frac{1}{3}$	1 3 $\frac{1}{3}$
$\frac{1}{3}$	$\frac{1}{3}$

Page 39

1 4 $\frac{1}{4}$	1 4 $\frac{1}{4}$
1 4 $\frac{1}{4}$	1 4 $\frac{1}{4}$
$\frac{1}{4}$	$\frac{1}{4}$

Page 40

$\frac{1}{2}$ $\frac{1}{3}$ ($\frac{1}{4}$)	($\frac{1}{2}$) $\frac{1}{3}$ $\frac{1}{4}$	$\frac{1}{2}$ ($\frac{1}{3}$) $\frac{1}{4}$
$\frac{1}{2}$ ($\frac{1}{3}$) $\frac{1}{4}$	$\frac{1}{2}$ $\frac{1}{3}$ ($\frac{1}{4}$)	($\frac{1}{2}$) $\frac{1}{3}$ $\frac{1}{4}$
$\frac{1}{2}$ $\frac{1}{3}$ ($\frac{1}{4}$)	$\frac{1}{2}$ ($\frac{1}{3}$) $\frac{1}{4}$	($\frac{1}{2}$) $\frac{1}{3}$ $\frac{1}{4}$
$\frac{1}{2}$ ($\frac{1}{3}$) $\frac{1}{4}$	$\frac{1}{2}$ $\frac{1}{3}$ ($\frac{1}{4}$)	($\frac{1}{2}$) $\frac{1}{3}$ $\frac{1}{4}$

Page 41

4 o'clock 4:00	1 o'clock 1:00	12 o'clock 12:00
9 o'clock 9:00	3 o'clock 3:00	11 o'clock 11:00
6 o'clock 6:00	10 o'clock 10:00	7 o'clock 7:00

Page 42

half past 3 3:30	half past 4 4:30	half past 5 5:30
half past 10 10:30	half past 4 4:30	half past 7 7:30
half past 6 6:30	half past 12 12:30	half past 9 9:30

Page 43

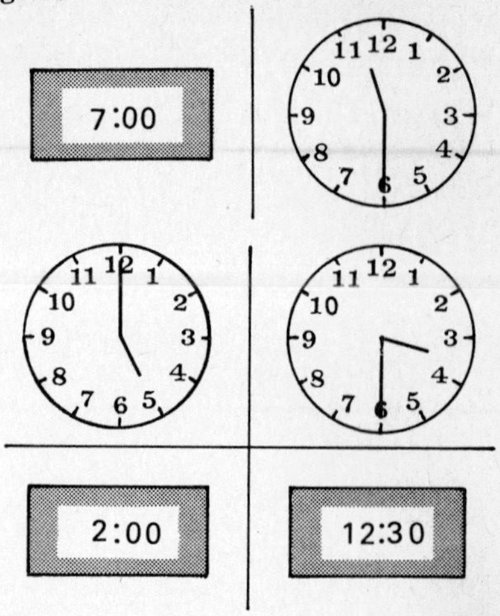

Page 44

3
12
3 o'clock

8
12
8 o'clock

12
4
4 o'clock

10
12
10 o'clock

6
1 2
1:30

Page 45

31 4 7 14 5 Thursday

Page 46

12 4 7 February 3 4

Page 47

2 5
10
4 7

Page 48

5	1
7	4
11	10
8	13

Page 49

1 2
4 3
6

Page 50

2 7
4
2 1
3
5
4

Answers for SPECTRUM MATHEMATICS (Brown Book, Third Edition)

Page 53

17	12	16	12	18	12
13	15	14	14	13	10
13	15	10	10	12	11
9	2	5	8	6	5
4	5	8	8	7	1
7	5	8	8	4	9

Page 54

5 + 6	9 + 2	7 + 9	9 + 7
4 + 7	8 + 3	8 + 8	
8 + 7	6 + 9	8 + 5	7 + 6
7 + 8	9 + 6	9 + 4	6 + 7
15 − 8	13 − 6	17 − 9	15 − 7
14 − 7	16 − 9	12 − 4	13 − 5
		11 − 3	
13 − 7	14 − 8	16 − 7	13 − 4
12 − 6			18 − 9

Page 55

6 tens	60		8 tens	80
40	60	60	70	80
50	70	70	80	20
30	80	90	90	80
90	50	40	90	60

Page 56

20	10	30	40	60
+30	+20	+50	+20	+30
50	30	80	60	90

Page 57

37		57	93	73
95	57	58	95	69
95	69	84	86	97
98	76	89	89	64
81	92	74	77	80

Page 58

25	14	21	31	41
+34	+12	+28	+24	+37
59	26	49	55	78

Page 59

77	76	50	44	78
65	59	94	85	78
77	86	97	98	95
79	37	66	99	96
59	49	55	48	78
96	98	65	22	49

Page 60

Rod
Pam

25¢ +20¢ 45¢	20¢ +32¢ 52¢
26¢ +20¢ 46¢	32¢ +26¢ 58¢
25¢ +32¢ 57¢	20¢ +25¢ 45¢

Page 61

2 tens	20		2 tens	20
20	40	10	40	0
40	60	40	10	10
30	30	50	70	20
10	10	30	20	30

Page 62

70	20	60	80	40
−30	−10	−30	−50	−30
40	10	30	30	10

Page 63

73		30	41	30
64	16	93	41	14
47	25	43	60	13
12	10	27	42	57
18	32	82	43	62

Page 64

65¢ −42¢ 23¢	45¢ −42¢ 3¢
42¢ −32¢ 10¢	65¢ −32¢ 33¢
65¢ −45¢ 20¢	45¢ −32¢ 13¢

Page 65

8	8	8	9	9	9
50	60	60	50	80	
58	35	99	67	67	
77	94	87	89	85	

Page 66

35	86			88	7	68
I	T			W	A	S
86	58	58		9	7	59
T	O	O		F	A	R
86	58		88	7	47	39
T	O		W	A	L	K

Page 67

50¢ +25¢ 75¢	50¢ +30¢ 80¢
25¢ +20¢ 45¢	50¢ +40¢ 90¢
50¢ 25¢ +10¢ 85¢	50¢ 25¢ +20¢ 95¢

Page 68

30¢ +34¢ 64¢	50¢ −30¢ 20¢
34¢ +25¢ 59¢	89¢ −25¢ 64¢
30¢ +25¢ 55¢	97¢ −34¢ 63¢

Page 69

67	87	39	70	78	99
48	67	70	98	79	75
35	86	59	97	87	60
81	33	44	50	10	10
16	25	44	22	10	23

Page 70

24	60	55	44	14
+43	−40	−24	+53	23
67	20	31	97	+32
				69

Page 73

13	14	17	13	12	11
15	13	11	18	15	16
70	50	68	75	85	98
9	6	9	5	2	9
9	8	8	7	7	7
10	50	62	32	53	10

Page 74

12	11	14	12	12	13
16	13	12	14	15	11
60	80	95	97	98	57
8	9	9	6	8	8
8	5	7	8	3	3
20	20	35	53	52	23

Page 75

73	32	83	87	93
61	55	64	91	95
91	85	82	74	92

Page 76

51	73	82	92	65
77	85	86	91	63
83	62	91	84	74
92	83	41	82	85
81	82	92	62	75

Page 77

47	83	41	75	93
55	92	82	56	53
96	62	76	80	73
52	53	81	74	36
74	66	41	90	77

Page 78

16	26	46	29	26
+18	+37	+39	+43	+14
34	63	85	72	40

Page 79

91	42	95	92	62
41	54	93	42	61
84	76	87	54	73
72	90	91	63	71
74	53	72	73	81

Page 80

36	35	63	48	29
+28	+28	+29	+35	+47
64	63	92	83	76

Page 81

35	35	19	26	28
37	37	48	8	19
16	16	36	28	16
28	16	25	14	17

Page 82

15	38	45	46	37
18	9	6	49	24
19	8	24	15	75
56	45	26	19	16
36	27	54	37	17

Page 83

19	25	18	77	35
18	16	8	14	17
29	27	58	17	38
7	14	18	18	36
19	7	38	18	35

Page 84

23	32	66	34	72
−19	−15	−39	−15	−44
4	17	27	19	28

Page 85

69	45	37	36	5
27	26	46	26	19
7	17	13	25	27
26	25	37	9	5
16	47	36	26	15

Page 86

40	36	57	84	74
+45	−18	−29	−69	−37
85	18	28	15	37

Page 87

93	83	43	90	67
71	51	53	75	82
72	71	91	84	57
28	8	19	45	18
68	68	18	35	23
59	27	44	18	14

Page 88

64	13	34	62	62
−29	+18	−19	+29	−45
35	31	15	91	17

Page 91

1 2 3 123	1 6 8 168
1 4 5 145	1 1 7 117
150	172
104	199

Page 92

2 7 9 279	4 3 0 430
3 5 6 356	3 0 0 300
236	340
499	289
404	321

266, 267, 268, 269, 270, 271
399, 400, 401, 402, 403, 404

Page 93

5 2 0 520	6 0 0 600
621	714
553	697
678	732
765	583
610	776
799	588

Page 94

8 2 5 825	9 1 6 916
928	842
892	903
975	840

200, 300, 400, 500, 600, 700, 800
870, 880, 890, 900, 910, 920, 930

Page 95

864	538
315	983
101	427

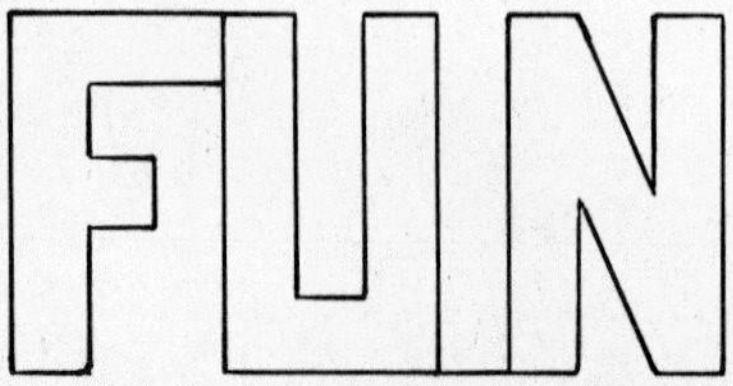

Page 96

420	819	770
302	325	345
144	607	159
855	256	199
210	173	422
689	761	949
580	940	666
994	500	180
630	848	799
800	584	594

Page 97

4	400	8	800
400	800	900	900
700	900	800	900
600	700	700	500
600	600	800	300

Page 98

300	500	100	400	200
+200	+400	+600	+100	+500
500	900	700	500	700

Page 99

768		779	
757	599	594	494
877	893	699	768
655	778	916	889

Page 100

342	403	210	135	536
+201	+426	+432	+143	+423
543	829	642	278	959

Page 101

565	786	829	954
398	487	874	688
934	978	897	785
579	895	757	789
869	788	698	970

Page 102

236	131	427	582	122
+250	+268	+370	+206	+76
486	399	797	788	198

Page 103

2	200	2	200
400	100	500	300
100	100	400	200
800	400	400	200
300	100	600	300

Page 104

400	300	900	800	700
−100	−200	−700	−300	−200
300	100	200	500	500

Page 105

833		444	
212	237	311	223
152	521	255	511
236	152	200	512

Page 106

568	732	635	386	874
−345	−412	−421	−32	−532
223	320	214	354	342

Page 107

504	411	182	424
313	223	272	330
514	822	831	154
131	232	233	751
634	100	272	540

Page 108

787	673	459	569	342
−535	−341	−138	−203	−132
252	332	321	366	210

Answers for Pretests and Checkups for SPECTRUM MATHEMATICS (Brown Book, Third Edition)

Page 9

6	10	9	8	5	4
7	6	10	6	10	3
4	7	9	7	9	10
0	3	4	7	4	5
8	1	1	2	3	2
3	1	3	2	1	4

Page 10

15		23		19
13			20	
34			46	
80			79	
9	10	11	12	
27	28	29	30	
53	54	55	56	
70	71	72	73	

Page 19

28		50	
31		45	
70		82	
66		98	
90		79	
7	8	9	10
40	41	42	43
56	57	58	59
64	65	66	67
81	82	83	84
89	90	91	92

Page 20

7	9	10	9	10	8
12	11	13	12	13	11
14	15	15	13	16	14
3	1	2	6	3	7
4	7	6	8	9	3
9	8	9	7	9	9

Page 35

13	13	14	17	11	14
13	18	15	16	16	15
5	8	3	4	8	5
9	9	8	9	3	7

$\begin{array}{r}9\\+6\\\hline 15\end{array}$ $\begin{array}{r}14\\-8\\\hline 6\end{array}$

Page 36

$\frac{1}{4}$	$\frac{1}{3}$	$\frac{1}{2}$
4 o'clock	half past 9	8 o'clock
4	7	
3	2	

Page 51

4		7
$\frac{1}{3}$	$\frac{1}{2}$	$\frac{1}{4}$
3		2
10:00	5:30	1:30

Page 52

50	70	90	80	50
78	75	82	97	96
7	6	60	70	90
30	40	30	10	30
61	53	66	51	33

Page 71

68	97	70	99	96	88
8	69	95	87	97	78
12	51	33	70	31	30
11	24	15	46	41	51

$\begin{array}{r}53¢\\+32¢\\\hline 85¢\end{array}$ $\begin{array}{r}68¢\\-44¢\\\hline 24¢\end{array}$

Page 72

42	33	41	55	92
70	91	91	60	82
41	61	44	51	80
24	6	17	9	19
49	37	17	24	4
13	19	16	28	16

Page 89

42	83	75	81	57
62	92	82	92	31
26	29	19	24	18
45	9	7	34	17

$\begin{array}{r}26\\-18\\\hline 8\end{array}$ $\begin{array}{r}26\\+36\\\hline 62\end{array}$

Page 90

532	841
486	378

400	900	500	700
689	678	657	639
100	700	200	100
525	152	314	324

Page 109

105	964
618	327
371	719

499, 500, 501
470, 480, 490, 500

800	800	597	249

Page 110

447	927	889	867
300	600	410	501
402	612	430	244

$\begin{array}{r}275\\-123\\\hline 152\end{array}$ $\begin{array}{r}212\\+84\\\hline 296\end{array}$

Page 111

46	80			
29	30	31		
94	95	96		
40	50	60	70	
9	5	7	10	3
12	18	11	11	16
13	17	15	12	14

Page 112

3	2	3	5	2
8	8	8	5	9
5	9	4	9	8
10	2			

$\frac{1}{2}$ ($\frac{1}{3}$) $\frac{1}{4}$ | $\frac{1}{2}$ $\frac{1}{3}$ ($\frac{1}{4}$) | ($\frac{1}{2}$) $\frac{1}{3}$ $\frac{1}{4}$

10:00 6:00 3:30

Page 113

10	7	15	16	13	17
80	69	97	8	60	87
84	53	91	700	897	699
3	4	5	9	8	7
50	18	10	16	81	16
49	28	14	113	114	234

Page 114

52	305	
89	736	
60	958	
50	51	52
296	297	298
70	80	90
530	540	550

Page 115

8	4
1	2

$\frac{1}{2}$ $\frac{1}{3}$ ($\frac{1}{4}$) | $\frac{1}{2}$ ($\frac{1}{3}$) $\frac{1}{4}$ | $\frac{1}{2}$ $\frac{1}{3}$ ($\frac{1}{4}$)

10:00 9:30 4:30

Page 116

$\begin{array}{r}25¢\\-22¢\\\hline 3¢\end{array}$ $\begin{array}{r}34¢\\+30¢\\\hline 64¢\end{array}$

$\begin{array}{r}34¢\\-30¢\\\hline 4¢\end{array}$ $\begin{array}{r}25¢\\+34¢\\\hline 59¢\end{array}$

$\begin{array}{r}34¢\\-25¢\\\hline 9¢\end{array}$ $\begin{array}{r}22¢\\+30¢\\\hline 52¢\end{array}$